Yorkshire's own kitchen

The guide to the best food and drink from Yorkshire and Humber

deliciouslyorkshire®

Acknowledgements

Our passionate Yorkshire chefs, Rosemary Shrager, Brian Turner, James Martin, Morrissey Fox, Andrew Pern, Richard Walton-Allen, Stephanie Moon, James Mackenzie; and Yorkshire champions the Archbishop of York, Alan Titchmarsh, Rosie Winterton MP and all members and staff of the Regional Food Group. Edited by Jane Chamberlain; copy Kindred; design and images Words&Pictures.

Published by the Regional Food Group for Yorkshire and Humber, Tadcaster Yorkshire.

Printed and bound by Pindar on FSC stock using environmentally-friendly inks.
A CIP catalogue record for this book is available from the British Library.

ISBN 978-0-9556344-1-3

Contents

Foreword

Jonathan Knight
Chief executive
Regional Food Group

Yorkshire boasts a culture rich in food and drink. The spectacular countryside of the Dales, Moors and Wolds coupled with the region's breathtaking coastline provide the backdrop to the production of some of the nation's most popular and well known products.

We're blessed to count cheese, lamb, beef, pork, ham, baked goods, pies, fish and chocolate among our historic culinary strengths. These are now complemented by an ever increasing use of innovation in the sector, which ensures Yorkshire is leading the way when it comes to producing high quality, value for money, local fare.

Our producers are truly passionate about what they do, and more and more people are turning to locally-sourced, in-season produce, which is paying dividends for the wider regional economy, not to mention the reduction in food miles and the benefit that brings to our wonderful Yorkshire environment.

It's important our local greengrocers, butchers and bakers are supported, and a growing appetite for farmers' markets and other food-focused events demonstrates the worth of our producers who, frankly, are inspirational. They are providing more and more food direct to our homes, online, and through the top notch restaurants and eateries that you'll find in this deliciouslyorkshire guide and which are committed to using local produce on their menus wherever possible.

The deliciouslyorkshire guide is a celebration of all things food and drink in Yorkshire, but it especially honours the champions working across the region's industry whether producing, selling or cooking our glorious food! Now more than ever, we need to be supporting the region's food and drink industry.

Find out more – and discover some mouth-watering recipes – at www.deliciouslyorkshire.co.uk

Buy local, think deliciouslyorkshire

deliciouslyorkshire encapsulates what the region's food and drink industry is all about: high quality, innovative, seasonal and local produce.

Since its launch, the brand has become increasingly recognised by consumers, and is used by producers the length and breadth of the region.

More and more people want to know where their food is from and deliciouslyorkshire tells consumers in an instant that the produce they are buying is local, fresh and has full traceability.

A truly distinctive Yorkshire experience isn't complete without a lovingly made full 'Yorkshire' using fresh, local ingredients. Look out for the deliciouslyorkshire breakfast symbol. Run by the Regional Food Group with Welcome to Yorkshire (formerly the Yorkshire Tourist Board), the scheme demonstrates food and drink establishments' commitment to using at least five locally-sourced ingredients – sausages, eggs, bacon, yoghurt, granola – in their breakfast menus.

The annual ***deliciouslyorkshire awards***, now in their fifth year, celebrate the pinnacle of fantastic regional food and drink and recognise the people behind it. Accolades are awarded in a range of categories which showcase best produce, best retailers, best hospitality.

So check out the 2008-2009 award winners throughout this guide. They provide more than just a flavour of the many dedicated professionals who make Yorkshire food and drink among the best you'll find in the UK.

www.deliciouslyorkshire.co.uk

"It was marvellous being a deliciouslyorkshire judge as I was in great, experienced company with rhubarb producers rubbing culinary shoulders with retailers, chefs and supermarket buyers"

Nigel Barden

deliciouslyorkshire Awards 2008-2009 judge and BBC Radio 2 resident foodie

deliciouslyorkshire®

AT
SWINTON PARK

“It’s not surprising Yorkshire is one of the largest food and drink producing regions in the country... just take a look in this wonderful guide to see what’s going on in God’s own county! We’ve got everything from cheese and chutney-making to sweets and salads to venison and vegetables – all produced by people with a passion for their work and a commitment to delivering the very best in regional food and drink. What an inspiration!”

Rosemary Shrager

“Being a Yorkshireman and a chef you understand the importance of great produce – and Yorkshire is an area rich and diverse in all types of food”

James Martin

What to eat

What to eat isn't an easy question to answer in Yorkshire and Humber – because there's so much fantastic food to choose from!

Without doubt this is the place to sample golden Yorkshire puddings, creamy curd tarts and succulent York ham for which the region is renowned. But don't mistake the enduring popularity of Yorkshire's traditional fare for evidence that its culinary tastes are stuck in the past.

The entrepreneurial spirit of food producers with a passion for flavour has turned the region into a gastronomic hothouse whose products are sought after by discerning palates throughout the UK and overseas.

Thousands of acres of the richest soil produce an array of fresh fruit and seasonal vegetables, while strong husbandry means animals are reared naturally in the outdoors on grassland – resulting in the best tasting lamb, venison, pork and beef on the market.

Glorious food

Curry Cuisine

deliciouslyyorkshire winner – Best Spice, Herb, Oil, Condiment or Preserve

Former accountant Prett Tejura created Curry Cuisine out of a passion for cooking delicious Indian food, a desire to pass on the tradition to her three children and a delight in helping others impress their friends and family with authentic home-cooked Indian meals.

The Leeds-based company she now runs with husband Paresh combines an array of award-winning products with a menu of cookery courses – either in customers' own kitchens or at the couple's Tingley home.

Curry Cuisine's range of 11 custom-made spice mixes – available online – includes the correct blends for favourite dishes such as aloo gobi matar, onion bhaji and chicken masala, taking the heat out of preparing the genuine article for the home cook.

The company's home-made salad dressings and pickles meanwhile have triumphed. Their Yorkshire-grown aubergine pickle was named Best Spice, Herb, Oil, Condiment or Preserve at the ***deliciouslyorkshire awards***, while their rhubarb and mango pickle – made with Oldroyd's rhubarb from the Yorkshire rhubarb triangle – was runner up. Prett said: "We use local produce wherever we can so that our products combine real Indian authenticity with true British provenance."

The cookery school, which offers one-to-one sessions, small group demonstrations and corporate team-building events, is expanding in 2009 to provide courses relating to dishes from different Indian regions.

Prett added: "Through the various cookery lessons and products on offer, I want to show everyone that cooking Indian food is easy, fun and exciting."

www.currycuisine.co.uk
(Contact details on page 177)

deliciouslyorkshire winner

Holme Farmed Venison

deliciouslyorkshire winner – Best Fresh Meat, Game or Poultry

Yorkshireman Nigel Sampson returned to his roots in 1990 following two years of deer farming on the island of Jura on the West Coast of Scotland – and launched Holme Farmed Venison, producing award-winning prime venison from animals naturally reared and grazed on traditional grassland.

Today Nigel has a staff of 30, a purpose-built production facility in Sherburn-in-Elmet and a herd of 2,000 native red deer, which he manages on his own farm near York and a number of associated farms.

He puts success down to two things: firstly, the quality and full flavour of its products, including its Rack of Venison which was named Best Fresh Meat, Game or Poultry in the ***deliciouslyorkshire awards***, and secondly the emergence of venison as 'the new beef'. "Venison has shrugged off its claret and tweed image and has become very popular as a healthier, lower fat alternative that's naturally high in omega 3 fatty acids and versatile enough for both the summer barbecue and the winter roast or casserole," said Nigel.

Holme Farmed Venison is also available all year round, enabling the company to deliver a consistent and constant supply of quality venison products, including joints, steaks, medallions, burgers, sausages and grills to leading supermarkets, farm shops, hotels and restaurants. The company also provides a mail order service to private customers. Nigel said: "As consumers become more concerned about where their food comes from and what's in it, our traditionally-reared, healthy, low fat meat fits the bill perfectly."

www.hfv.co.uk

(Contact details on page 86)

deliciouslyorkshire winner

"Venison has shrugged off its claret and tweed image and has become very popular as a healthier, lower fat alternative"

J. Stringer & Son

deliciouslyorkshire winner – Best Bakery Product, including Bread, Cakes and Biscuits

The Stringer family has farmed on the Yorkshire Wolds for more than half a century, converting their land at High Callis Wold, Bishop Wilton, to organic farming in 1999.

Its crops and livestock are produced using a system which minimises artificial inputs and places a high emphasis on animal welfare. Lambs are reared outside and fed on spring grass and red clover to produce a full flavoured, tender meat. They are also slaughtered and butchered locally, reducing both the stress on the animal and food miles.

The company also produces flour, bread mixes and porridge oats from organic cereals grown and milled on the farm using a traditional wooden mill. The wheat grown for flour is mainly Maris Widgeon – an old variety with lots of flavour ideally suited to organic farming – and Stringer's organic bread mix won the prize for Best Bakery Product, including Bread, Cakes and Biscuits at the ***deliciouslyorkshire awards***.

The farm was the first in the Yorkshire Wolds to grow certified seed potatoes and now produces a range of seed potatoes for farmers and gardeners, choosing varieties that have good flavour and low susceptibility to disease. It also supplies organic table potatoes which are sold at the farm gate, farmers' markets in York and Leeds and a number of small independent stores in and around York.

Partner Mark Stringer, son of founder John, said: "Our aim as organic farmers is to improve the natural fertility and soil structure of the land, which we feel has deteriorated over the last 50 years. The improvement of both these things is reflected in the high quality products we produce."

highcalliswold@aol.com

(Contact details on page 75)

deliciouslyorkshire winner

"When awards judges tell you they loved the product so much that they took the leftovers home after judging, you know you must be doing something right!"

Shepherds Purse Cheeses

deliciouslyorkshire winner – Best Dairy Product and deliciouslyorkshire Champion

Shepherds Purse Cheeses began life in 1987 on the kitchen table of Judy Bell's farmhouse in Thirsk when the former pharmaceutical technician had the idea of developing cheeses made from sheep's milk for people with bovine intolerances.

Two years later, Fine Fettle (formerly Yorkshire Feta) and Olde York were officially launched at the Great Yorkshire Show and the tributes started to flow.

In 1994, Shepherds Purse diversified to produce a blue cheese made from cow's milk, becoming the first company to reintroduce blue cheese making to Yorkshire since its disappearance from the county in the 1960s.

The multi award-winning Yorkshire Blue – winner of Best Dairy Product at the ***deliciouslyorkshire awards*** and Gold Medal winner at the World Cheese Awards – now accounts for 75 per cent of the company's total production and is available through all the major multiples' deli counters as well as quality independent wholesalers, delis and gastro hotels.

Judy said: "When awards judges tell you they loved the product so much that they took the leftovers home after judging, you know you must be doing something right!"

Shepherds Purse also produces other speciality blue cheeses including Mrs Bells Blue, named after Judy and produced using 100 per cent locally sourced ewes milk, and Buffalo Blue made with Italian Water Buffalo milk.

Alongside the blues is the Ryedale range – a traditional English cows milk cheese matured for four to six months and available plain or with a variety of intriguing marinades – and Monks Folly made to an ancient recipe believed to have been used by local monks.

www.shepherdspurse.co.uk
(Contact details on page 81)

deliciouslyorkshire winner

“A hedge that’s good for sloes is a hedge that’s good for the birds and butterflies”

Sloe Motion

deliciouslyorkshire winner – Best Confectionery, including Sweets and Chocolates

What started as a hobby for environmentalist Jonathan Curtoys has turned into an award-winning business creating traditionally made liqueurs and chocolates from berries that grow naturally on the hedgerows of North Yorkshire.

Jonathan, who has a degree in agriculture, and former business partners Richard and Julia Brown had the idea of harvesting sloes from the hedges of Manor Farm, Eddlethorpe and making gin as a sideline. Because the blackthorn fruits on the previous year’s growth, it also meant the hedgerows wouldn’t be cut every year, creating a haven for local wildlife.

What they didn’t anticipate was the enormous success of Sloe Motion, which is now a full-time enterprise based at Green Farm, Barton-le-Willows, supplying sloe gin, vodka, whisky, chocolates and even sloe chutney to more than 150 delicatessens and farm shops throughout the UK, including at Castle Howard, Chatsworth, Harvey Nichols, Weetons and Daylesford Organics.

The sweet and fruity gin with a dry finish was named Best Drink in the Taste of Britain Awards, while the chocolate truffles, made from 35 per cent fruit smothered in Belgian chocolate won the title Best Confectionery, including Sweets and Chocolates in the ***deliciouslyorkshire awards***.

The company’s need for sloes is now such that Jonathan encourages other North Yorkshire farmers to manage their hedges so that the blackthorn can flourish. He said: “For hedgerows to produce sloes they need to be left uncut for at least a couple of years. This means that a hedge that’s good for sloes is a hedge that’s good for the birds and butterflies. That sounds like a win-win.”

www.sloemotion.com

(Contact details on page 78)

deliciouslyorkshire winner

Stuart's Foods

deliciouslyorkshire winner – Best Fresh Produce

Stuart and Brenda Howarth enjoy eating out but in the mid 1980s they were often disappointed by the tasteless frozen chips served to them in restaurants. When they asked why fresh potatoes weren't used, chefs told them they simply didn't have time to prepare them – so the Scarborough couple rented a small unit in the East Coast town and set about preparing fresh chips for local eateries.

It wasn't long before chefs asked for carrots and other vegetables to be similarly supplied. Stuart's Foods never looked back. Today Stuart, Brenda, and their children Damian and Samantha are all directors of the family business sourcing, preparing and supplying fresh quality vegetables, fruits and dairy products to schools, hospitals, hotels and restaurants across Yorkshire and Humber region.

They also support other Yorkshire food companies by supplying a range of local products that includes soups from The Yorkshire Provender, sausages from Masham Sausages and puddings from Just Puds. In its 21st anniversary year, the company was named Large Producer of the Year in the ***deliciouslyorkshire awards***.

A year later its celebrated roast vegetable mix took the prize for Best Fresh Produce 2008-2009. The judges said: "Kids who get to eat these are really lucky."

Now operating out of a 5,000 sq ft facility in Scarborough and employing 23 people, Stuart's Foods has built an enviable reputation for quality produce, realistic pricing and real customer service. Stuart said: "Our team all share my passion for quality fresh food and our customers know they can depend on us to 'go that extra mile'."

www.stuartsfoods.co.uk

(Contact details on page 84)

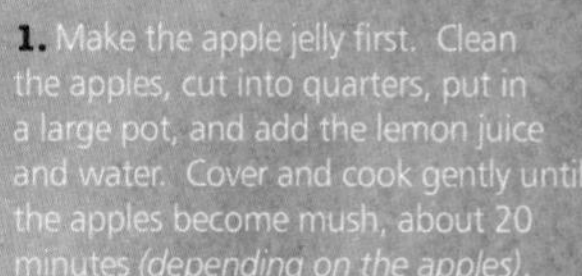

Recipe

Black Pudding Toast with Apple Jelly

Serves 4

Ingredients

350g (12 oz) black pudding
bacon fat, to fry 4 slices
wholemeal bread

Apple jelly

1.3kg (3 lb) green apples,
skinned juice of ½ lemon
1.2 litres (2 pints) water
granulated, caster or
preserving sugar

Brian Turner

Method:

1. Make the apple jelly first. Clean the apples, cut into quarters, put in a large pot, and add the lemon juice and water. Cover and cook gently until the apples become mush, about 20 minutes *(depending on the apples)*.

2. Put into a jelly bag or a conical sieve lined with muslin suspended over a bowl, and allow to drain, preferably overnight. Try hard not to push and poke, but allow the juice to come through naturally, so as to get a clearer jelly.

3. Measure the juice and add 450g *(1 lb)* sugar for every 600ml *(1 pint)* of juice. Put into a clean pan and simmer gently until the sugar has dissolved. Boil rapidly, stirring frequently and skimming off any scum that arises, until setting point is achieved, after about 15 minutes. If ready, take off the heat, pour into clean jars, and leave to set.

4. Cut the black pudding lengthways into slices to match the length of the bread. However, if you can only do rounds, cut as thinly as you can. *(Slices are easier to eat than rounds.)* Heat the fat and gently fry the black pudding until coloured and cooked, about 5 minutes. Drain well on kitchen paper.

5. Meanwhile toast the bread, and take off the crusts. Spread the bread with a little apple jelly, lay the cooked black pudding on top, and cut the bread in half lengthways. Spoon a little apple jelly on each toast and serve.

Whitby Seafoods

deliciouslyorkshire winner – Best Fish and Seafood, Smoked, Cured or Fresh

Founded in 1985 by Graham Whittle, Whitby Seafoods is a leading scampi producer specialising in the supply of seafood products to the food service and retailers.

The company is built on strong ethics and focuses on sourcing as much raw material from local fisheries as possible and supporting the sustainability of the local scampi catch. To this end the company has recently sponsored the South North Sea fisheries in entering assessment by the Marine Stewardship Council (MSC) with the goal of attaining MSC certification for sustainability.

The business now employs 140 local people at a state-of-the-art facility in the famous fishing town of Whitby and supplies 3,300 tonnes of frozen seafood a year to its customers, including many familiar retailers such as Lidl, Farm Foods, Heron Frozen Foods, Makro and selected Tesco, Sainsbury and Asda stores.

In addition to classic succulent scampi, Whitby Seafoods produces a wide variety of flavourful alternatives including hot 'n' spicy prawns, garlic and ginger prawns, a variety of fish cakes and Whitby fillet goujons – named Best Fish and Seafood, Smoked, Cured or Fresh in the ***deliciouslyorkshire awards***.

Graham said: "We at Whitby Seafoods are proud to continue the fine Whitby fishing tradition by creating, delicious, high-quality, local products from sustainable sources."

www.whitby-seafoods.com

deliciouslyorkshire winner

> We realised our supreme quality malting barley and own water supply were the basis for excellent beer

Wold Top Brewery

deliciouslyorkshire winner – Best Drink, Alcoholic, Non-Alcoholic, Tea or Coffee

Before farmer Tom Mellor set up the Wold Top Brewery in 2003, the only experience he had of beer making was the odd dabble with a home brewing kit. But necessity, they say, is the mother of invention, and the need to diversify in order to pay the bills at his 600 acre arable farm in Wold Newton, gave him the idea of establishing a micro brewery using quality home grown malting barley and the purest chalk filtered water from the farm's own borehole.

Six years on Tom and wife Gill's award-winning traditionally made cask and bottled real ales are the toast of East Yorkshire, regularly featuring in the press and broadcast media. Their Wold Top Bitter was winner of Best Drink, Alcoholic, Non-Alcoholic, Tea or Coffee at the ***deliciousyorkshire awards*** and was rated third in a TV quest to find Yorkshire's perfect pint. Even their latest gluten free beer Against the Grain has been voted 'the most beer like' by taste test participants.

Tom said: "We just looked at the raw ingredients we had and we realised that our supreme quality malting barley (processed at a local maltsters in Castleford) and our own water supply were the basis for excellent beer."

In addition to supplying cask ales to pubs and clubs, Wold Top has a range of bottled all year round ales and limited edition ales available through independents and farmers' markets. They also produce seasonal ales and bespoke beers for local events.

A range of Wold Top's beers are also available to buy online in cases of 12 bottles or a gift pack selection of four bottles. Against the Grain gluten free beer is available to order online at www.ale4home.co.uk

www.woldtopbrewery.co.uk
(Contact details on page 135)

deliciouslyorkshire winner

W. S. Bentley (Growers)

deliciouslyorkshire winner – Award for Innovation

High quality, pesticide-free salad cress has been grown by three generations of the Bentley family at Gomersal over more than five decades.

Every week sees three crops of their unique product – a delicate mix of cress and rape seedlings creating a balance between spiciness and crunchiness – produced at their two-hectare site, resulting in the distribution of ten million punnets a year to supermarkets, wholesalers, distributors and caterers.

More recently, the company added nutty tasting alfalfa sprouts and a selection of high-fibre, high-protein sprouting mixed beans (adzuki beans, chick peas, lentils and mung beans) to its offering under its new own washed and ready-to-eat label '…and sow on…'. The diversification, which required substantial investment in new food grade premises and equipment, led to W. S. Bentley picking up the Award for Innovation at the ***deliciouslyorkshire awards*** and the brand is now selling well in Booths, selected Co-operative stores, Waitrose in Yorkshire and northern branches of Spar. This year saw still more additions to the fold in the form of alfalfa and leek seedlings and sprouting peas.

Managing director Jan Bentley puts Bentley's continued success down to its loyal staff, even the oldest members of which have a totally open approach to change. "Our people are fantastic and have a habit of staying with us for a long time," he said. "Their flexibility has enabled us to adapt to and cater for modern tastes, contemporary lifestyles and healthy eating."

www.andsowon.co.uk
www.wsbentley.co.uk

deliciouslyorkshire winner

MoFo Mussels

serves 4 as a starter

Ingredients

2 kg live mussels
250ml Morrissey Fox Blonde
150ml double cream
2 tbsp chopped parsley
½ onion, finely chopped

Method:

Firstly prepare the mussels: rinse under cold water, scraping off any barnacles and pulling off the beards. Tap any mussels that are open, and if they don't start to close up, discard them. Rinse again, and store in a container in the fridge covered with a damp, clean tea towel.

To cook the dish, simply heat a heavy based saucepan with a tight fitting lid, throw in the mussels, onion and Blonde and put on the lid. Give the pan a shake every minute or so. The mussels are ready as soon as they have fully opened. At this point just pour in the cream, bring back to the boil, add the parsley and serve with plenty of crusty bread – to mop up the delicious sauce.

Richard Fox and Neil Morrissey, Ye Olde Punch Bowl

Yorkshire Dales Meat Company

deliciouslyorkshire winner – Best Prepared Meat

The Knox family has farmed for over 100 years in the foothills of the Yorkshire Dales at Mill Close Farm, Bedale, rearing rare breed sheep and cattle – including Aberdeen Angus – and growing their own feed.

Today farmer-turned-producer Stephen Knox and his 10-strong team combine their excellent animal husbandry with that of other Dales farmers to provide a range of consistently full-flavoured 'gate to plate' products.

Since substantial investment in a state-of-the-art cutting facility, the Yorkshire Dales Meat Company has become a 'must have' supplier for quality hotels, restaurants and gastro pubs throughout the North of England, as well as a number of leading supermarkets.

In addition to primary beef, pork, lamb, poultry and game, the company's 'Flavour of the Dales' range includes marinated products, handmade burgers and sausages with classic flavour combinations such as lamb and mint or venison and cranberry. It was the Heavenly Honey Swaledale Sausage, produced using organic Swaledale lamb, sticky Yorkshire honey and home-grown rosemary and garlic, that scooped the award for Best Prepared Meat at the ***deliciouslyorkshire awards***.

Despite now being recognised as one of the best catering butchers in the region, the company still loyally attends local farmers' markets and food fairs. Stephen said: "It gives us a chance to talk directly to the people who eat our food: listening will always be a vital core ingredient."

www.yorkshiredalesmeat.com
(Contact details on page 89)

deliciouslyorkshire winner

"Attending local farmers' markets gives us a chance to talk directly to the people who eat our food: listening will always be a vital core ingredient"

Deliciously yours

Take Yorkshire's finest fresh produce, blend it with the passion and creativity of top chefs and add that unique special ingredient – you.

Whether it's an indulgent weekend brunch, a light lunch for all the family or a master chef-inspired foray into fine dining, great home-made food puts heart in the house and is a welcome gift to those you care about.

Dip in to these inspiring recipes because eating in is the new eating out and you're lucky enough to be in Yorkshire…

More inspirational recipes on
www.deliciouslyyorkshire.co.uk

Mackenzies Yorkshire Smokehouse

Based in the heart of the Yorkshire Dales, Mackenzies is an award-winning family business specialising in the production of high quality smoked and cured foods. Take a trip out to Blubberhouses and visit the shop and highly acclaimed restaurant.

Warm salad of smoked duck, crispy pancetta, orange segments and baby potatoes

Serves: 4

Ingredients

1 fillet Mackenzies smoked duck
100g Mackenzies pancetta
½ red onion
1 whole orange
6 cherry tomatoes
6 cooked baby potatoes
1 bag *(200g approx)* mixed Mediterranean style lettuce
Raspberry vinaigrette dressing
salt & black pepper *(optional)*
2 – 3 tablespoons olive oil

Method

Peel the orange; remove all pith and pips, cut into segments
Finely slice Mackenzies smoked duck fillet
Dice Mackenzies pancetta
Slice cooked baby potatoes into approx 1cm slices
Finely slice red onion
Halve the cherry tomatoes
Place the mixed leaves, sliced red onion, halved cherry tomatoes and orange segments in a large bowl.
Add the raspberry vinaigrette and gently mix to thoroughly coat the leaves with dressing.
Heat the oil in a frying pan, add the diced pancetta and fry till crisp, add the sliced potatoes and brown slightly on both sides.
Add the sliced smoked duck and gently warm through.
Drain any excess oil from the pan and add the smoked duck, potatoes and pancetta to the bowl of salad ingredients. Gently mix all the ingredients together taking care not to break the potatoes.
Serve immediately with some fresh crusty bread and a glass of wholesome red wine, the choice is yours.

(Contact details on page 124)

Brazilian Flavours

Isabel Gordon

The ingredients used in Brazilian Flavours products are all responsibly sourced, from the flours used in our 'Pão de Queijo Mix' (cheesebreads snacks) and Pizza Base Mix to the very exotic Guava and Cashew fruits used in our preserves, we aim to offer coeliacs, and non-coeliacs alike, interesting and great-tasting natural foods, using ingredients celebrated for their beneficial properties. Our home-baking mixes are naturally gluten and wheat free, No artificial preservatives, flavours, colours or hydrogenated fats. Suitable for vegetarians and low in salt.

Swaledale Mature Cheddar Cheesebread Bites (gluten & wheat free)

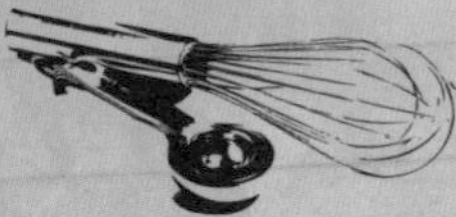

Serves: 4
Baking time: 25 minutes

Ingredients

250g of Isabel's cheesebread mix
100g Swaledale Mature Cheddar cheese
160ml water
1 large egg
2 ½ tbs olive oil

Method

Pre-heat oven to 200°c *(180°c fan assisted ovens or Gas mark 6)*.
Pulse all the ingredients in a food processor *(including the cheese)* until it comes together into a ball, then turn out the dough into a bowl.
Take small pieces of the dough and roll into small balls of about the size of a fifty pence piece *(30mm diam)*.
Place on a non-stick baking tray 2 cm apart. Bake for about 20-25 mins, or freeze and bake them direct from frozen later on if you wish.

(Contact details on page 168)

Crayke Kitchen

Soft fruit and champagne jelly

These champagne jellies really do celebrate our wonderful soft fruit. They are very simple to prepare, taste and look splendid, and will keep well for a couple of days in the fridge.

Ingredients

350ml *(12 fl oz)* champagne or sparkling dry white wine *(Cava)*
250g *(9oz)* caster sugar
1 x 11g powdered gelatine or 2 sheets leaf gelatine
mixed soft fruit

Method

Heat the champagne with the sugar and stir until the sugar has dissolved. Soak the gelatine in cold water then add to the wine. Leave the mixture to cool, then chill until it is on the verge of setting.

Use 4- 6 *(depending on size)* individual dariole moulds or ramekins and arrange a layer of soft fruit across the bottom. Pour in enough cold jelly to just cover the fruit and return the mould to the fridge to set. Once this layer has set add another layer of fruit and jelly and continue like this until the mould is full.

Chill the jellies for a couple of hours before serving.

(Contact details on page 203)

Tiffin Foods UK

Whitby Landed Crab and Yorkshire Cranberry

Whitby landed crab, organic watercress with a rich and fruity cranberry chutney on a Yorkshire Baked Tiffini Bread

Ingredients

Yorkshire Tiffini Bread *(Fosters)* 100g
Whitby Landed Crab 90g
Organic Watercress 50g
Cranberry Chutney *(Shaws Pickles)* 40g

(Contact details on page 177)

The Butchers Arms

Pan roast loin of Round Green Farm venison served with a little venison cottage pie

Pan roast loin

Ingredients

100g venison loin
1 x sprig of thyme
1 x sprig of rosemary
½ garlic clove roasted
pinch of pepper
10ml rape seed oil
2 juniper berries
½ tsp Womersley Apple and Thyme Jelly

Method

Trim all sinew from the venison loin.
Tie with string to form a round compact steak.
Lay out a piece of cling film and drizzle with the oil, season with pepper and place the sprigs of rosemary and thyme onto the seasoned cling film with the roast garlic and juniper berries.
Place the venison loin onto the cling film and wrap tightly to season and marinade.
Leave in the fridge until required.
Pan fry until golden brown (about 4 minutes on each side)
After cooking place on Apple and Thyme jelly.

Venison cottage pie

Ingredients

1 shallot finely chopped
20g carrot finely chopped
20g celery finely chopped
20g leek finely chopped
½ garlic finely chopped
10g mushroom sliced
1 x sprig of thyme
1 x bay leaf
1 x sprig rosemary
200ml venison stock
100g venison mince
Red wine
Rape seed oil
Potatoes
Butter, cream and 1 egg yolk

Method

In a pan brown the venison mince, remove.
Sweat the vegetables in a pan and then add the browned venison mince, tie the herbs to make a bouquet garni and place into the mince.
Add the red wine and reduce, then add the venison stock.
Peel the potato and boil until soft drain and mash.
Mix in the cream, butter and egg yolk.
Place into a piping bag with a star nozzle.
When the mince has reduced, season to taste and place into copper pan.
Pipe the creamed potato on top and place into a hot oven to brown the potato.

(Contact details on page 182)

Ingredients

200g Yorkshire Blue
1 x red pepper
3 x medium tomatoes
1 x clove garlic
1 x cup of water
1 x sprig of rosemary
½ x dried chilli
1 x small onion
1 x stick celery
2 x bay leaves
Pinch cracked black pepper
100g Yorkshire dry cured bacon
1 x tbs of balsamic vinegar
1½ x glass of Leventhorpe Madeline white wine
225g x Carnaroli risotto rice
3 x tbs of rapeseed oil
100g x black pudding
1 x pear
60g x mixed salad leaves
A dash of Yorkshire Relish

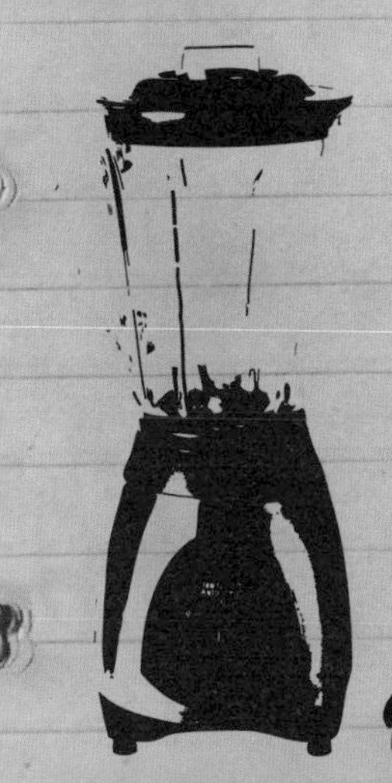

Yorkshire Risotto starter

Method

Blend together the tomatoes, red pepper, garlic, chilli, rosemary, water in to a smooth liquid.
Add balsamic vinegar and pepper and blend again
Chop celery and onion and slice the bacon
Cook on medium heat with 1 tablespoon of rapeseed oil until the onions are translucent in colour.
Add bay leaves and stir for 3 – 4 minutes
Add rice and stir, add wine and stir for a further 4 minutes.
Stir and blend stock – leave to simmer
Poach the black pudding
Peel the pear and poach in ½ glass of wine and cover with water for 10 minutes
Add 2 tablespoons of rapeseed oil to the risotto.
Add the cheese.
(Save some to sprinkle on top before serving)
Put salad on plate & chop pear in salad, crumble black pudding on leaves and Yorkshire relish dressing.
Place risotto on plate with cheese sprinkled on top to garnish.

(Contact details on page 171)

Ulrick + Short

Half fat blueberry muffins with Delyte 5

Makes 12 Muffins

Cooking time 20 – 30 Mins
10.8% Fat (Compared to 19.2% fat if all butter used)

Ingredients

110g/4oz plain flour
22g/¾oz Delyte 5
55g/2oz butter
65g/2½ caster sugar
2 eggs
1½ tsp baking powder
125g/4½oz blueberries
33ml/2tbsp water
Pinch nutmeg

Ulrick&Short US

Method

1. Cream the butter and sugar together then slowly add the eggs and water and mix for 3 minutes. Add the flour, Delyte 5, baking powder, nutmeg and mix. Slowly mix in the blueberries.
2. Place a spoonful of mixture into each muffin case, filling each just over halfway.
3. Bake in an oven set at 200°C/400°F/Gas 6 for 20 minutes or until golden on top.

(Contact details on page 173)

The Cooking School at Dean Clough

Pandora's pudding

Ingredients

125g caster sugar
500g rhubarb – trimmed and cut into 2cm lengths
500ml whipping cream
2 tbs Cointreau

Method

1. Put the sugar and rhubarb in the pan. Place the lid on. Gently heat for 10 – 12 minutes *(stir it after 5 – 6 minutes)* until it is soft and the juices are released.
2. Take the pan lid off and simmer for 20- 25 minutes until a thick purée forms. Stir it at intervals to prevent sticking. Place the cooked rhubarb in a mixing bowl and allow to cool.
3. Place the cream and Cointreau in a large bowl and whisk it until it is stiff. In three lots, fold in the cold rhubarb to give a streaky marbled effect.
4. Transfer to either a glass bowl, a serving plate or 4 – 6 serving glasses. Chill until required.

(Contact details on page 179)

"It was a delight to taste such an inspiring range of food produced in Yorkshire, reflecting traditional methods alongside modern techniques"

Nigel Barden

deliciouslyorkshire Awards 2008-2009 judge and BBC Radio 2 resident foodie

"The produce from Yorkshire gets better and better. This guide tells the world where to find it and who makes the best!"

Brian Turner

Where to buy it

As any chef knows, the finest dishes need the very best ingredients – and God's own county of Yorkshire – and Humber – is abundant in the natural supply of excellent quality fruit, vegetables, crops, livestock and seafood.

Buying local is a great way to support the region's economy, and consumers are guaranteed high quality, value for money produce with full traceability.

Just about every village, town and city boasts specialist grocery stores and butchers where you can buy flavoursome local meat or seasonal fruit and vegetables, and the revival of traditional farmers' markets, farm shops and country shows means you can often buy produce direct from the very people who did the raising and nurturing in the first place.

And many producers now sell online via their own websites or use the sourcing section of www.deliciouslyyorkshire.co.uk to locate that vital ingredient.

Go for local

Balloon Tree, Gate Helmsley

deliciouslyorkshire winner – Award for Farm Shop Retailer of the Year

It was the Machin family's enthusiasm for fresh produce that led to it setting up The Balloon Tree Farmshop and Café in 2004 at the farm where it had successfully grown soft fruit and vegetables for more than 20 years.

The goal was simple – to sell the freshest quality produce direct to the consumer, staying competitive by cutting out middlemen and distribution costs.

Five years on, The Balloon Tree at Gate Helmsley is a favourite foodie destination operating under the mantra: "Fewer food miles, more farm yards". It's also the winner of numerous accolades including the title Farm Shop Retailer of the Year in the ***deliciouslyorkshire awards*** for two years running.

Established by Digby and Jill Machin, the shop, delicatessen and café are now managed on a day-to-day basis by the couple's sons Will and Matthew who pride themselves on offering a wide range of 'super-fresh' fruit and vegetables grown on site, together with traditional rare breed meat including Longhorn cattle and Gloucester Old Spot cross pigs. You can also buy their gran's award-winning chutney as well as home-made ready meals, free range eggs and locally produced cheeses, ice-cream, honey and preserves.

Save some room though for the award-winning cakes and puds produced in the bakery by chief baker Phyllis and sold through both the shop and café.

'Pick-your-own' fans are spoilt for choice in the summer months with strawberries, raspberries, gooseberries, redcurrants, blackcurrants, white currants, blackberries, blueberries and even pulling peas, broad beans and runner beans."We're passionate about quality local food and we are always striving to make our customers' experience enjoyable and unique," said Will.

www.theballoontree.co.uk

(Contact details on page 125)

deliciouslyorkshire winner

Weeton's, Harrogate

Changing the flagging fortunes of British farming is the philosophy underpinning Weeton's – Harrogate's urban farm shop.

The shop, described as 'spectacular' by *The Independent* newspaper, is listed as one of the 'top 100 shops in the world' by the *Daily Express* and voted one of the 10 Best Butchers in England by the *Meat Trades Journal*. "If you looked up the term 'foodie heaven' in the dictionary, a photograph of Weeton's would do as a definition," said *The Observer*.

In a bid to highlight the great and the good of local food and drink, Weeton's stocks over 800 locally produced goods and supports over 50 family farms by stocking and promoting their produce and giving a direct and more profitable route to market. If you are looking for the best meat, bread, cheeses and vegetables sourced locally in Yorkshire, Weeton's is the place.

Since opening in 2005, the shop has welcomed more than half a million customers through its doors and has directly spent over £1 million with local livestock farmers. Weeton's even farms its own herd of pedigree beef cattle near Ripon, ensuring full traceability, great tasting meat and a minimum of food miles.

Owner Andrew Loftus said: "Locally-sourced food makes sense for farmers and customers. It benefits the rural economy, reduces food miles and simply tastes better."

www.weetons.com

(Contact details on page 124)

"Locally-sourced food makes sense for farmers and customers. It benefits the rural economy, reduces food miles and simply tastes better"

Recipe

Cheese Pudding

Ingredients

1 cup breadcrumbs *(very coarse)*
1 cup strong Wensleydale cheese
1 cup milk
1 egg

Rosie Winterton
Minister for Yorkshire

Method

Mix ingredients together
Take a shallow dish and melt 1 ounce of butter
When sizzling, pour mixture into the dish and bake for 40 minutes at 200°c

Rosie says: "It's my Yorkshire grandmother's recipe and it's like soufflé but thicker!"

Yorkshire Deli, Ilkley

The Yorkshire Deli Café and Shop in West Yorkshire's elegant spa town of Ilkley sells a wide variety of quality produce from across God's own county.

Yorkshire brack and gingerbread from Botham's of Whitby, extra virgin cold pressed rapeseed oil from Wharfe Valley Farms at Collingham, honey from the Denholme Gate Apiary at Bradford – all can be found in this fine food emporium that goes out of its way to source everything locally wherever possible, even down to the furniture, photographs and paper bags!

You'll find everything you'd expect, such as Taylor's Yorkshire Tea and Farrah's Original Harrogate Toffee, as well as one or two surprise delights like sparkling wine from the Leventhorpe Vineyard near Leeds and Bare Earth dry cured beef biltong, originally created by South African tribesmen and now adapted by a couple in Melmerby to produce a wholesome, low-fat snack. Many products are also available from the Yorkshire Deli's online store launched in September 2007.

The deli café produces mouth-watering home-cooked food using the best Yorkshire ingredients, but for those on the move, it also puts together nutritious packed lunches for walkers and picnic hampers for alfresco meals in the summer sun.

Partner Ian Taylor said: "Our philosophy is to support producers, suppliers and small businesses as local to the café as possible, but not to compromise on quality in doing so. We can't claim to be perfect in our quest, but we think we've made a pretty good stab at it – and we aim to be constantly improving."

www.yorkshiredeli.co.uk

(Contact details on page 181)

Round Green Farm, Barnsley

Round Green Farm started deer husbandry in 1979 and converted from dairy to deer in 1985. Having been discovered by Waitrose and Tesco in the 1990s and Sainsbury in 2004, it has a unique high welfare BRC accredited abattoir.

As suppliers to both the catering industry and retail outlets, Round Green's product range extends to steaks, joints, racks, casserole, mince, liver, sausages, burgers, pies, pâté and smoked venison.

Farmer Richard Elmhirst's work with award-winning chefs includes researching new products with Jeff Baker of J. Bakers at York, combining deer farm tours with lectures and cookery demonstrations by Tim Bilton of the Butchers Arms at Hepworth.

Careful study of wild deer and their habits has enabled Round Green Farm – where the deer are mostly red with some fallow – to copy the free ranging lifestyle of the animals while at the same time taming them to accept human contact, all of which leads to unstressed stock and tender, long shelf-life products.

Richard said: "Customers are very welcome at the farm and shop and many enjoy combining a visit with a pleasant walk through the Round Green deer in Stainborough Deer Park."

www.roundgreenfarm.co.uk
(Contact details on page 154)

> "Farmer Richard Elmhirst's work with award-winning chefs includes researching new products with Jeff Baker of J. Bakers at York"

Ripley Store, Ripley

deliciouslyorkshire winner – Award for Independent Retailer of the Year

Ripley Store in the picturesque North Yorkshire village of Ripley sources the finest local foods and condiments from across Yorkshire. Among its offerings are cakes and tarts, an array of pies, Yorkshire cheeses, freshly baked bread, preserves, vegetables, fine wine and beer.

The store was named Independent Retailer of the Year in the ***deliciouslyorkshire* awards** 2008-2009.

(Contact details on page 80)

deliciouslyorkshire winner

Recipe

Yorkshire Brack

Elizabeth Botham coffee and cake shop of Whitby was where I first tasted Yorkshire Brack. It's a bit like a fruit cake but lighter and has the taste and texture of sticky toffee pudding. Botham's sell tea-infused or ginger flavour Brack and it's made fresh in the shop. While buying some of this stuff, try the lemon buns – it's what they are famous for and they taste bloody great. Then while walking round the town with a bag of Brack in one hand, sticky lemon bun in the other and dodging the seagulls, do the local thing: split the bun in half and turn the top over to make like a sandwich and munch away – you won't look too much like a tourist. Sorry almost forgot, buy two as it's a long walk back up the hill for another one!

Serves 6 to 8

Ingredients

1 lb 8oz sultanas
1 lb 8oz dark raisins
1 lb firmly packed light brown sugar
240ml cold strong breakfast tea
120ml whisky or bourbon
1 lb 4oz plain flour
4 tsp baking powder
1 lrg pinch salt
1 tsp grated nutmeg
1 tsp grated all spice
3 eggs, beaten
1 grated rind of 1 lemon

Method

1. Soak the raisins, brown sugar, tea and whisky in a large bowl for 12 hours or overnight.
2. The next day, sift together the flour, baking powder, salt, nutmeg, and all spice and add to the raisin mixture along with the beaten eggs and lemon rind.
3. Set the oven at 160°C/300°F. Put the batter into a greased 10 inch cake tin, and bake for 60 to 80 minutes until firm to the touch.
4. When done, remove from the pan and let cool on a rack. You can leave it simple and serve it with butter or put a little icing on the top.

James Martin

"My mother spends her time growing amazing fruit and vegetables here at Burton Agnes and at my brother's hotel – Swinton Park, in North Yorkshire"

Burton Agnes Hall Farmer's Food Store, Driffield

Burton Agnes Hall and Gardens is an Elizabethan stately home with award winning gardens on the southern edge of the Yorkshire Wolds, close to the market town of Driffield.

The Farm Shop opened in 2006, selling fruit and vegetables picked from the walled garden alongside a fantastic range of locally-produced food, confectionery gifts and snacks.

It sells fresh, seasonal produce from Yorkshire including Burton's pork, Ridings Reserve beef and Burdass lamb, local eggs and flour and East Yorkshire honey. It also sells a range of smoked foods, goats' and cows' cheeses, cakes, puddings and soups along with Yorkshire jams and pickles.

The farm shop, hall and estate are managed by Simon Cunliffe-Lister, who inherited the estate 15 years ago, aged 12, and now lives at the hall with his wife and two children.

"My mother spends her time growing amazing fruit and vegetables here at Burton Agnes and at my brother's hotel – Swinton Park, in North Yorkshire," he said. "There's no way we can eat everything she makes, so a farm shop is an obvious outlet. We are lucky to have such a wealth of delicious local produce to add to this."

www.burton-agnes.co.uk

(Contact details on page 140)

Where to eat

> “Yorkshire has acquired a great reputation for the quality of its produce and for its skill in turning that produce into meals fit for a king. No longer can Yorkshire be accused of being a ‘meat and two veg and nothing fancy’ part of Britain. When it comes to producing the finest cuisine, Yorkshire is way out in front”
>
> Alan Titchmarsh

With such a bountiful supply of fresh local ingredients, it’s no surprise that some of the greatest ever chefs either hail from Yorkshire and Humber or choose to spend their time here creating mouth-watering dishes for lucky citizens and visitors.

The region has more Michelin-starred restaurants and more independent breweries than anywhere else in the country. Culinary prowess is not, however, confined to fine dining at sizzling city venues where you’ll find a wealth of formal occasion restaurants, relaxed brasseries and smart café tearooms.

A growing number of gastro pubs are also successfully combining the best of traditional British pub hospitality with imaginative award-winning menus using locally-sourced ingredients such as Yorkshire lamb and rare breed beef.

And be sure to check out some of the fantastic eateries opened by local farmers who are quite literally offering a ‘gate to plate’ service with fruit and vegetables picked fresh on the day.

> "We make sure every visit to our tea rooms is a memorable one"

Bettys Café Tea Rooms, Harrogate

Bettys Café Tea Rooms are the pride of Yorkshire, using skills handed down through the generations and standing for quality and elegance.

Ninety years after young Swiss confectioner Frederick Belmont opened the first Bettys in Harrogate, the business is still a family concern that remains true to his founding principles that everything should be 'fresh and dainty' and that 'if we want things just right we have to do them ourselves'.

There are six Bettys Café Tea Rooms to explore: two in Harrogate, two in York, one in Northallerton and one in Ilkley. Recent extensive refurbishment of the flagship Harrogate branch has included restoration of the first floor Imperial Suite – closed to the public for 40 years – and the addition of the Montpellier Café Bar, which has a distinctly continental style.

Dishes on the café menus are freshly made from locally-sourced ingredients where possible and there is something for every time of day, be it a full evening meal, afternoon tea, or morning coffee and croissants.

All have shops too, which offer an extensive range of cakes, breads, biscuits and chocolates made by hand at Bettys Craft Bakery in Harrogate, as well as fine teas and coffees blended by sister company Taylors of Harrogate.

Bettys general manager June Wood said: "Our commitment to keeping Bettys small and special means that we can keep a watchful eye on every detail – and make sure every visit to our tea rooms is a memorable one."

www.bettys.co.uk

(Contact details on page 93)

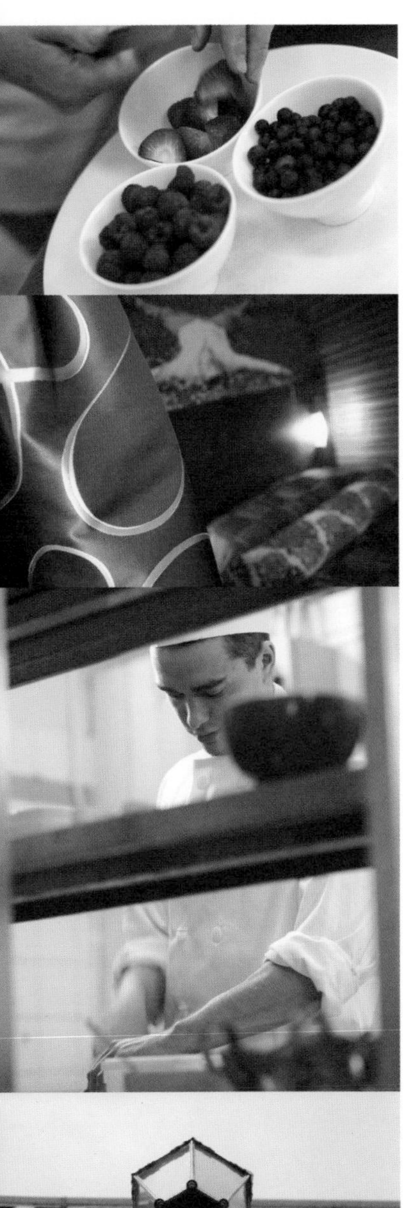

The Crown Hotel, Bawtry

The Crown Hotel at Bawtry has charmed guests since it was a coaching house in the 18th century, but the warm welcome afforded by The Crown of today involves a much more luxurious and creative environment.

Over the last three years, The Crown has benefited from a £4 million transformation that has created 76 modern and opulent bedrooms – one of which was recently included in *The Times* Top Ten most outrageous hotel rooms in Britain – and four excellent air conditioned and Wi-Fi equipped meeting rooms.

The creativity is not however confined to the décor, and the mouth-watering culinary designs of The Crown's talented kitchen team have pleased the discerning palates of many a stylish traveller, including TV personality Gok Wan and pop phenomenon Boyzone.

The mood in the restaurant is modern rustic, combining sleek tables and leather booths with log features and unique modern art. Dishes are created by a talented kitchen team using local produce delivered daily from a network of renowned high quality producers, including prime cuts of beef from local farmer Gerard Farmer's award-winning breed of Red Poll cattle.

Head chef Caroline Rhodes said: "I'm a big believer in knowing where our food comes from, which is why I always try to use fresh local produce whenever possible. We are proud to be part of the deliciouslyorkshire brand and we actively promote the distinct and diverse variety of Yorkshire produce."

www.crownhotel-bawtry.com

(Contact details on page 159)

"We are proud to be part of the deliciouslyorkshire brand and we actively promote the distinct and diverse variety of Yorkshire produce"

The Pipe and Glass Inn, South Dalton

In the 15th century, the gatehouse to Dalton Park offered visitors to the great house hospitality and lodgings during their stay. Today the Pipe and Glass Inn stands on the same spot and similarly promises its visitors a warm Yorkshire welcome.

Described by *The Guardian* newspaper as a 'genial heaven', it has numerous awards to its name including a ***deliciouslyorkshire award*** for Best Use of Local Produce on a Menu. It was also voted overall winner in the Taste of England Awards 2009.

Chef James Mackenzie and his wife Kate took over the inn, parts of which date back to the 17th century, in 2006 and immediately undertook a full refurbishment. While the couple were careful in ensuring the bar retained its wonderful country pub feel, they gave the restaurant a more contemporary look with bespoke wooden tables – including a spectacular 24-placer – and a conservatory looking out over the garden.

The sumptuous traditional menu changes regularly but always includes great locally-sourced ingredients such as James White's pork sausages accompanied by bubble and squeak and ale and onion gravy, or baked Lowna dairy goat's cheese tart with honey roast beetroot, red chard and hazelnut pesto.

And don't miss out on the Pipe and Glass chocolate plate – five very good reasons to love chocolate!

The wine list is also sourced entirely from small producers, and there's a wide selection of regularly changing hand-pulled ales, ciders and guest beers from local micro breweries. James said: "I'm committed to sourcing as much local and seasonal produce as possible – but first and foremost it's quality that counts."

www.pipeandglass.co.uk

(Contact details on page 143)

"I'm committed to sourcing as much local and seasonal produce as possible – but first and foremost it's quality that counts"

Recipe

Forced Yorkshire Rhubarb trifle with rum soaked parkin crumbs

Makes 4 glasses

Ingredients

8 sticks of
forced pink rhubarb
caster sugar
Grenadine

For the pastry cream

250ml milk
4 egg yolks
65g caster sugar
½ vanilla pod (split)
1 knob of ginger

For the chantilly cream

500ml double cream
½ vanilla pod (split)

toasted almonds
icing sugar
4 pieces of 'Parkin' or ginger cake
Rum

Parkin

200g self raising flour
4 tsp ground ginger
2 tsp ground nutmeg
2 tsp ground mixed spice
150g oats, 200g syrup
50g black treacle
200g butter
200g soft dark brown sugar
2 eggs (beaten)

Method

To make the parkin heat the syrup, butter, treacle and sugar in a large saucepan. Then add the flour, oats, eggs and mix. Pour into a grease proof lined baking tray and cook for 10 – 12 minutes @ 160˚C. Remove from oven and cool in tray.

Cut the forced rhubarb into 2 inch pieces and place in deep baking tray, pour approximately 100ml of water over. Sprinkle with castor sugar, depending on how sweet you want it, then pour 4 – 6 dashes of grenadine over and cover with tin foil. Bake in the oven at 180˚C for about 10 – 15 minutes until just poached. Remove tray from oven and cool, leaving the rhubarb in the poaching liquor. When the rhubarb has cooled pour off the poaching liquid into a saucepan and reduce to a syrup, then cool.

To make the custard, whisk the egg yolks and sugar, add the flour and whisk. Bring the milk to the boil with the vanilla and ginger, pour over the egg mix. Whisk and return to the pan, cook over a moderate heat for about 5 minutes constantly stirring with a wooden spoon. Pour the cooked custard mix into a bowl and cover with cling film to prevent a skin forming. Cool in refrigerator. Whip the double cream with 50g of icing sugar and the vanilla seeds to soft peaks. Fold 1/3 of the whipped Chantilly cream through the custard.

To make the trifles, crumble some parkin into the bottom of a glass and pour on some rum – as much as desired!!! Then spoon in some of the poached rhubarb followed by the custard, then spoon or pipe some of the cream on top. Finish with the rhubarb syrup, toasted almonds and a dusting of icing sugar. If you don't want to make the parkin you could use some bought ginger cake.

James Mackenzie

Recipe

Yorkshire asparagus with Poached Egg ravioli, parmesan

Serves 2

Ingredients

1 bunch Yorkshire asparagus trimmed
200g pasta flour
6 free range Yorkshire eggs
olive oil
small block parmesan
salt and white pepper

Method

To make the raviolis first

Around three hours before serving

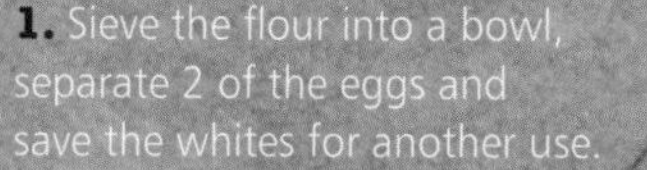

1. Sieve the flour into a bowl, separate 2 of the eggs and save the whites for another use.
2. Mix one whole egg with the 2 egg yolks and pour this onto the flour, add 1 tablespoon of cold water and mix into smooth stiff dough.
3. Knead well by hand until fully soft and pliable *(this can take 15 minutes)*.
4. Now to prepare the raviolis, roll the pasta into long thin sheets in a pasta machine.
5. Cut large disks of the sheets with a espresso cup saucer.
6. You will need 4 large disks.
7. Crack the 2 eggs carefully into a small container, now place the first disk onto the saucer and carefully pour the egg into the dip in the middle of the disk.
8. Place another disk carefully on top and seal around the edge by firmly pressing down *(the raviolis will now keep for a couple of hours in a fridge)*.

Finishing touches

1. Bring a large pan of water to the boil and add plenty of sea salt
2. Cook your asparagus until tender but not floppy (depending on the size around 4-6 minutes), take out the asparagus and pop on warm plates, and carefully put the raviolis into the boiling water and time 1 minute 30 seconds
3. Remove the raviolis with a slotted spoon, drain well and season with salt, white pepper and olive oil, and place carefully on top of your asparagus
4. Shave parmesan onto the plates and a little olive oil to finish

Richard Walton-Allen

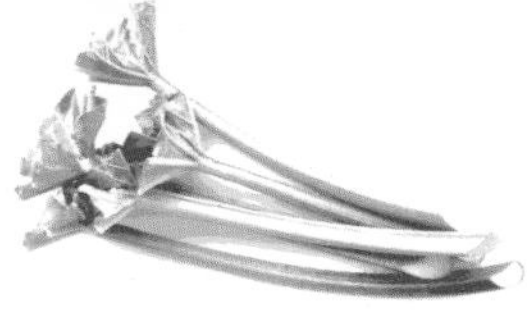

Harvey Nichols Fourth Floor, Leeds

Harvey Nichols' first store outside London opened in the historic Victoria Quarter of Leeds in 1996, instantly becoming a landmark destination in the city centre.

Situated on the top floor is the unique Fourth Floor Café – ideal for a stylish breakfast, lunch or afternoon tea with spectacular views over the rooftops of Leeds, or for an evening dinner when the rest of the store is closed. In the summer, the restaurant's floor-to-ceiling windows open onto a balcony used for alfresco dining.

Yorkshire-born executive chef Richard Walton-Allen is known for using seasonal ingredients as well as sourcing the highest quality produce available regionally. He has developed long-term relationships with regional suppliers and is himself an avid 'home-grown' fan, growing vegetables on his allotment.

Richard's creativity and passion for food have led to the Fourth Floor winning numerous awards and the menu is updated every six weeks using staples like organic flour from Ripon, breads from Garforth, and meat from Yorkshire farms. In 2009, to celebrate his first ten years at the helm, Richard has created a tasting menu incorporating the best of the decade and inspired, he says, by 'great produce and a wandering palate'.

Included on the anniversary menu are Yorkshire goat's cheese and slow cooked onion tart, north coast cod fillet pea and bacon sauce, crushed lemon artichokes, ravioli with beetroot and horseradish, grilled ox tongue, pavé of sea trout, slow cooked Dales shin beef with anise and ginger, Bok choi and mushrooms, brûlée baked apple and the unbeatable Yorkshire blue cheeses with heather honey.

The Fourth Floor's wine list is also one of the most extensive in the country, packed with an array of well-known labels and hidden gems.

www.harveynichols.com

(Contact details on page 193)

Clocktower Restaurant, Rudding Park, Harrogate

deliciouslyyorkshire winner – Award for Best Use of Regional Produce – Restaurant, Hotel, Pub or Inn

The use of seasonal and local ingredients, combined with the stunning surroundings of Rudding Park, Harrogate make the Clocktower restaurant a must for all with a passion for food.

Served in a friendly, relaxed atmosphere and cooked and presented by a passionate team of award-winning chefs, the menus use fresh Yorkshire produce to offer modern British dishes with plenty of creativity.

Eat them seated beneath the striking pink glass chandelier from Nice, relax in the bright and airy conservatory alongside a 400-year-old olive tree, or simply enjoy a drink at the contemporary bar.

Their designer is executive chef Stephanie Moon, whose signature dish 'Yorkshire tapas' can be taken either as a light bite or as part of a meal. Another favourite, rack of Nidderdale lamb, travels just five miles from 'gate to plate', while the most popular dish from the bar menu is Whitby smoked haddock in Black Sheep beer batter.

In addition to its seasonal menus the Clocktower, which won the award for Best Use of Regional Produce – Restaurant, Hotel, Pub or Inn in the ***deliciouslyyorkshire awards*** 2008-2009, also offers a monthly Yorkshire menu. It hand-picks a local food hero from within a 75-mile radius of Rudding Park and champions their produce, creating a suitably delicious dish and annotating the food miles from food hero to Rudding Park on the menu.

Stephanie said: "We are a passionate team of chefs from around the world who are all ambassadors for Yorkshire food products. The fantastic local produce that comes into Rudding Park inspires us to create new dishes and the appreciative response from customers tells us that people really do care about where their food comes from."

www.ruddingpark.com
(Contact details on page 103)

deliciouslyyorkshire winner

Recipe

Whitby Crab, Crayfish and Avocado Cocktail Lacey's traditional cheese wafer

Serves 4

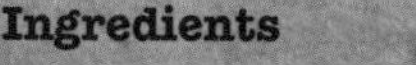

Ingredients

To create this dish you will need 4 Martini glasses
2 dressed Whitby crabs
(white crab meat only)
1 ripe avocado
20 cooked crayfish *(shelled)*
2 baby gem salad leaves
150g finely grated
Lacey's traditional cheese

For the dressing:
100 g caster sugar
Finely grated zest of 2 limes
(using a micro plane if possible)
juice of 2 limes *(passed through a sieve)*
water to mix

Method

To make the dressing:

Using a very clean pan *(If your pan is not very clean the sugar will crystallise)* and place the sugar in the pan and just cover with water.
Heat this until a thick syrup-like consistency is reached, and then add the lime juice and zest to the syrup. Allow this thick lime dressing to cool.

To make the cheese wafer:

Simply place the grated cheese on baking parchment or a silicone mat and bake gently at 160°C for 5 minutes until golden and crisp.
Remove from the tray and allow to cool.
Chefs note: This will not work with all cheeses but if you want an alternative, Parmesan cheese works really well.

To assemble the dish:

Wash, dry and polish your martini glasses and place on a tray.
Rinse and pat dry the little gem salad leaves with a clean cloth then shred with a knife and place into the bottom of the Martini glasses.
Pick through the cooked dressed Whitby crab *(discarding any shell)* and place on top of the little gem salad in each glass.
Place 5 crayfish on top of the crab-meat, then spoon over the lime syrup dressing.
Serve with the Lacey's Traditional wafer on the side of the glass.

Stephanie Moon

Recipe

Deep-fried Scarborough Woof with Seared Flamborough Sea Scallops, Warm 'Fortunes' Kipper Salad, Wild Garlic Mayonnaise

Serves 4

Ingredients

a little rapeseed oil
8 king scallops, cleaned and out of shells
12 x 50g pieces of woof
(cod if unavailable)
herbed breadcrumbs
eggwash *(egg whisked with a little milk)*
seasoned flour
8 wild garlic leaves for garnish

For the Wild Garlic Mayonnaise

Ingredients:

200ml basic mayonnaise *(3 egg yolks, 200ml rapeseed oil, 5ml white wine vinegar, 15g English mustard, 1 tsp granulated sugar)*
35g chopped wild garlic
Seasoning

Method:

Put the vinegar, mustard and egg yolk into a mixing bowl and whisk together, then slowly add the oil until the mixture thickens (if it becomes too thick, add a little warm water). Finely chop the wild garlic and mix in, then season to taste.

For the salad

Ingredients:

A few mixed leaves ie, peashoots, landcress, flat parlsey, etc
100g cooked kipper meat – boneless
(Fortunes is a famous Whitby Smokehouse situated near the foot of the '199 steps' in the shadows of Whitby Abbey.)
House vinaigrette

Method:

Make mayonnaise and set aside.
Cook kippers, remove bones, keep warm.

When all ingredients/components of the dish are assembled, the putting together of the dish is quite simple. Firstly heat a frying pan for the scallops. Coat the woof in seasoned flour, then in the eggwash, then into the herbed breadcrumbs, shake off the excess breadcrumbs, then dip into the fryer and deep fry at 180°C for 3 to 4 minutes, until golden brown. While these are cooking, season and sear the king scallops in a little rapeseed oil, colour lightly for approx 1 to 1 ½ minutes each side, dress the salad leaves add the warm kipper, then arrange in a wire basket or other suitable vessel, garnish with the dressed salad leaves and the mayonnaise. Serve immediately.

Andrew Pern

> It's a mix of spiced up old favourites and Anglicised classics – all using, wherever possible, seasonal produce from a strong network of both professional and amateur local suppliers

The Star Inn, Harome

Over the last 13 years Andrew and Jacquie Pern have turned a derelict thatched property into one of the finest Michelin-starred restaurants in Yorkshire, winning numerous awards and accolades along the way.

Described as 'the very model of an English pub' by the *Good Food Guide 2008*, The Star Inn was named Egon Ronay Gastropub of the Year 2006. More recently chef Andrew saw his first book, *Black Pudding & Foie Gras*, named Gourmand Awards UK Chef Book of the Year and the couple took the prize for Special Achievement at the Northern Hospitality Awards.

The emphasis at The Star, in the pretty rural setting of Harome, is on traditional English food with an original twist. Andrew said: "It's a mix of spiced up old favourites and Anglicised classics – all using, wherever possible, seasonal produce from a strong network of both professional and amateur local suppliers."

For example, you might start with a risotto of wild mushrooms with wilted baby spinach, white truffle oil and a little Hawes Wensleydale salad, and progress to a main course of pan-roast haunch of Duncombe Park roe deer with a little venison 'cottage pie', Scottish girolle mushroom and tarragon juices.

Jacquie runs front of house, welcoming guests to the couple's 'home' in a relaxed yet efficient approach to service in two dining rooms, the bar or, weather permitting, the garden.

In 2009 Andrew also began running one of the first ever chef's tables in a gastro pub, inviting guests to watch him produce an eight-course tasting menu from the best seasonal produce, and even take part in the cooking themselves.

www.thestaratharome.co.uk

(Contact details on page 119)

Cedarbarn, Pickering

deliciouslyyorkshire winner – Award for Best Use of Regional Produce in a Café/Tearoom

It's only two years since Mandy and Karl Avison opened the Cedarbarn Farm Shop and Café on the site of their family farm and PYO in Pickering, but already the enterprise has won the hearts of foodies across the county, winning the award for Best Use of Regional Produce in a Café/Tearoom in the ***deliciousyorkshire awards 2008-2009***.

Its entire ethos is one of good quality, traditional, wholesome food prepared with the finest ingredients and the farm's own or local produce wherever possible. "We also pride ourselves on a good old fashioned service with friendly helpful staff," said Mandy.

The menu and specials board reflects the farm's growing patterns – from asparagus in the spring to strawberries, raspberries, new potatoes and plums, while pure bred Aberdeen Angus beef has pride of place every day in dishes ranging from lasagne to sirloin steak. The Aberdeen Angus pies particularly have been recommended by local celebrity chef Annie Stirk in the *Yorkshire Post Magazine*.

On Sundays Mandy and Karl offer a very popular traditional Sunday lunch (for which booking is advisable), the highlight of which is of course their own roast Aberdeen Angus beef and home-made Yorkshire pudding. Other local specialities on the Sunday menu include home-made pate featuring smoked trout from Moorland Trout Farm at Pickering. In addition, the kitchen produces delicious cakes, scones, pastries and biscuits and Cedarbarn is licensed, enabling diners to enjoy a glass of wine or beer with their meal.

The eco-friendly, cedar-clad building, designed by Karl himself, is set in an attractive herb garden with a water feature – its large windows overlooking green fields, vegetable patches and rows of soft fruit. There's a safe place for children to play and an annual maize maze in August.

> "We also pride ourselves on a good old fashioned service with friendly helpful staff"

Mandy@topbridgefarm.freeserve.co.uk

(Contact details on page 102)

deliciouslyorkshire winner

Devonshire Arms Hotel, Bolton Abbey

The Devonshire Arms Country House Hotel and Spa has long been known as a place for food lovers. Situated on the Duke of Devonshire's 30,000 acre estate at Bolton Abbey, on the edge of the Yorkshire Dales, it attracts visitors from far and wide as well as being hugely popular with local diners from the nearby towns of Ilkley, Skipton and Harrogate.

There are two restaurants to choose from while morning coffee, light lunches and afternoon tea are served in the inviting lounges.

The Michelin-starred Burlington Restaurant, where head chef Steve Smith offers a choice of three menus, a la carte, a tasting menu and a ten-course prestige menu, is open for dinner Tuesday to Sunday and also for Sunday lunch. Steve's food offers diners an exciting journey of tastes and textures matched by an impressive selection of over 2,000 bins of fine and rare wines.

The Devonshire Brasserie and Bar by contrast is relaxed, informal and very colourful. Diners can choose to eat in the restaurant, bar or, in warm weather, outside, and it's open daily for lunch and dinner. Steaks, fresh fish, game, bangers and mash, sticky toffee pudding and a local cheese board are typical of the regularly changing menu – all complemented by an excellent wine list and locally brewed cask ales.

Steve said: "Throughout we use fresh, seasonal produce, sourced from the estate, nearby farms and local suppliers, and also from our own extensive kitchen garden, which provides vegetables, herbs and some soft fruit for both restaurants."

www.thedevonshirearms.co.uk
(Contact details on page 105)

Five of the best

It's official! According to *Harden's 2009 UK Restaurants Guide*, Yorkshire has the largest number of quality restaurants in the UK outside of London!

And they include five Michelin star restaurants – the most in any county in the north of England – using locally-sourced produce to deliver high quality, imaginative and mouth-watering dishes.

1. The Burlington Restaurant, The Devonshire Arms Country House Hotel & Spa, Bolton Abbey, North Yorkshire. Seasonal game and fish, all from the Bolton Abbey Estate, together with vegetables and herbs from the hotel's gardens, are the hallmarks of the restaurant's splendid menu.

2. The Star Inn at Harome, near Helmsley, North Yorkshire. A certain northern rooted-ness inspires Andrew Pern's cooking, where poet and peasant co-exist in one menu.

3. The Box Tree, 35 -37 Church Street, Ilkley, West Yorkshire LS29 9DR. The modern French classical menu and extensive wine cellar offer food lovers an unforgettable experience.

4. The Old Vicarage, Ridgeway, Sheffield, South Yorkshire. Michelin star chef Tessa Bramley's cooking is grounded in nature and evocative of the seasons. She is a country cook whose work revolves around her garden.

5. Yorke Arms, Pateley Bridge, near Harrogate, North Yorkshire. Michelin star chef Frances Atkins' cooking is based on simple ideas and well-tried combinations, but still contrives to introduce new twists and original touches.

Where to stay

“The bottom line is, if you come to Yorkshire you will get a great welcome and you will be fed and watered in style”

Gary Verity

Welcome to Yorkshire

Yorkshire and Humber's highly developed sense of hospitality is no secret. The region is traditionally characterised as offering a warm welcome via a glowing hearth and generous helpings of wholesome, satisfying food and drink.

Little has changed in this regard, however, the range and diversity of accommodation available today is broader than ever before – catering not only for every budget, but also every conceivable taste and requirement.

Across rolling hills and dales, in picturesque market towns and in beautiful seaside locations, you'll find individual B&Bs and guesthouses whose owners are passionate about providing all the home comforts, including hearty home-cooked food.

Just one step from vibrant city streets are countless award-winning hotels and, if history and architecture inspire you, you'll find a number of sumptuous country piles set in their own grounds – some retreats to be relished, others just a stone's throw away from exciting activities and great days out.

For more inspiration visit
www.yorkshire.com

Time to relax

Oulton Hall, Leeds

Eighteenth century Oulton Hall is the height of elegance and the only five star hotel in the North of England. The mansion, once home to the Blayds family, has had £20 million lavished upon it over recent years by De Vere Hotels and now features magnificent public areas and breathtaking grounds with service to match.

Visitors can expect to be waited on by butlers with high tea in the drawing room, sip chilled champagne in the stunning champagne bar or relax and unwind with a choice of 304 varieties of whisky in the new whisky snug.

The food philosophy is simple: 'Legendary local ingredients, prepared to perfection'. The Calverley Grill offers the classic best of British menus in sumptuous surroundings, while the Claret Jug, with views across the golf course and rolling Yorkshire countryside, offers a more relaxed, informal atmosphere with wholesome local food. For pure escapism, Oulton Hall has a new luxury spa where candlelit treatments, relaxation rooms and a VIP suite provide total peace and serenity. Alternatively you can take a 20ft putt on the park course under the watchful eye of the hotel's expert technical team in the academy.

Deputy general manager Scott Turner said: "At Oulton Hall we pride ourselves on delivering fantastic experiences and creating reasons for our guests to come and stay, with our fantastic restaurants, amazing spa and challenging golf course we feel we have the ultimate resort package whatever your reason for visiting us."

www.oultonhall.co.uk

(Contact details on page 187)

“The food philosophy is simple: 'Legendary local ingredients, prepared to perfection'”

Low Penhowe, Burythorpe

deliciouslyyorkshire winner – Award for deliciouslyyorkshire Breakfast Member

Former IT sales director Christopher Turner and his wife Philippa had no previous experience in the hospitality trade when they followed their dream and opened their home in Malton as a bed and breakfast six years ago.

It didn't prove a hindrance – the couple quickly won five-star status and a gold award from the English Tourism Council, and this year Low Penhowe was named Welcome to Yorkshire's Guest Accommodation of the Year and deliciouslyorkshire Breakfast Member 2008-2009.

The traditional stone-built Yorkshire farmhouse offers accommodation for up to six people in an idyllic spot with sweeping views of the Howardian Hills, Yorkshire Wolds and across the North Yorkshire Moors.

Home-cooked Aga breakfasts are a speciality and include the guesthouse's own free-range eggs with locally-cured bacon, black pudding and sausages from the butcher. Even the tomatoes and mushrooms are sourced locally. As an alternative, guests are offered locally-smoked kippers, smoked salmon with scrambled eggs and home-roasted York ham with poached eggs – all rounded off with home-made marmalade and jams, home-baked bread and honey from village farms.

"The breakfast is a major selling point with our customers," said Christopher. "They sing our praises and 50 to 60 per cent specifically mention the breakfasts – that is why we get so many bookings. If you're going to do something, you may as well do it properly."

www.bedandbreakfastyorkshire.co.uk

(Contact details on page 114)

deliciouslyorkshire winner

“Mount Pleasant is all about offering the finest local food items matched with excellent service and ambience”

Mount Pleasant Hotel, Doncaster

Set in 100 acres of beautiful woodland, the Best Western Premier Mount Pleasant Hotel is Doncaster's only AA four star rated hotel – and it exudes luxury from its every nook.

Just a mile from Doncaster Sheffield International Airport and handy for the races, it's a lavish retreat with two four-poster suites and 56 richly appointed ensuite bedrooms that happily blur the interface between traditional comfort and modern essentials like free satellite TV and Wi-Fi high speed internet access.

Seasonal menus and delicious dishes made from fresh local ingredients are the order of the day in the Garden Restaurant, winner of two AA Rosettes.

The hotel's expert chefs can also cater for private meals in one of four informal lounges, which are otherwise used to serve an array of light snacks, bar meals, afternoon teas, ales and beverages throughout the day.

The Mount Pleasant has six modern function rooms and three stylish bars for larger business gatherings or banquet events, which, together with eight luxury self-catering cottages, help make it a favourite wedding venue. The Therapié health and wellness centre was opened in 2006 and offers the ultimate in relaxation and pampering with products from Espa and Dermalogica.

General manager Richard Tyas said: "Mount Pleasant is all about offering the finest local food items matched with excellent service and ambience."

www.mountpleasant.co.uk

(Contact details on page 159)

Swinton Park, Masham

Swinton Park is a luxury castle hotel set in 200 acres of landscaped parkland, lakes and gardens in the Yorkshire Dales. It is the ancestral seat of the Earl of Swinton, and combines all the warmth and traditions of a stately home with every creature comfort you would expect of a contemporary hotel.

There are 30 individually designed bedrooms along with conference and wedding facilities and an exclusive use spa with five treatment rooms. An extensive range of country pursuits includes falconry, fishing, shooting, riding, golf and off-road driving and guests are invited to freely explore the grounds on the estate with a specially-prepared picnic.

The cookery school is a particularly popular attraction with residential courses run by celebrity chef Rosemary Shrager, and a range of day and evening courses are offered throughout the year. The hotel also runs Alfresco Food Festivals in the Parkland, with culinary trails and demonstrations in May and September.

The estate and hotel's four-acre walled garden has recently been restored, providing a wealth of cultivated and wild produce, which plays a prominent role in the restaurant menu and cookery course recipes.

Swinton Park restaurant, which serves modern British cuisine, has been awarded three AA Rosettes, placing it in the UK's top ten per cent. Lunch, refreshments and bar snacks are also available every day.

Lady Masham, Felicity Cunliffe-Lister, said: "History, tradition and the wonderful landscape surrounding us allow us to offer guests the unique opportunity to enjoy the authentic country house experience."

www.swintonpark.com

(Contact details on page 120)

Guinea Fowl with Herbs and Braised Fennel

Serves 4

Ingredients

2 plump guinea fowl
4 leaves sage
1 sprig rosemary
2 sprigs thyme
4 tablespoons chopped dry cured streaky bacon
juice of ½ lemon
olive oil, salt and pepper

Method *Oven 200°C*

First cook the dry cured streaky bacon. Chop the herbs and mix with salt and pepper, then stuff the guinea fowl with this mixture. Take a large sheet of foil and put it in a roasting tin, then lay the fowl on top, sprinkle with the lemon juice and olive oil and then close the foil tightly and roast for an hour, pulling back the foil for the last 20 minutes to allow the bird to brown.

Braised Fennel

4 small heads of fennel, trimmed and cut in quarters
40g butter
100ml chicken stock
4 tablespoons grated parmesan
salt and pepper

Blanch the fennel in boiling water for 3 minutes. Melt the butter in a pan large enough to take the fennel in one layer, then toss the fennel until it is beginning to colour. Add the stock, cover the pan and cook until tender, then remove the lid and reduce the stock till syrupy. Put into buttered gratin dish and sprinkle over the parmesan. Taste for seasoning – it may not need much salt but will need pepper. Bake in the oven for 15 minutes.

Rosemary Shrager

Tickton Grange, Beverley

Thirty years ago, Tickton Grange was a dilapidated country house with wet rot, dry rot, broken radiators, rotten floors, flooded cellars and fallen ceilings.

Today it is one of Yorkshire's favourite independent hotels thanks to the vision, dedication and downright hard graft of Peter and Sheila Whymant, their family and the enthusiastic team they have built around them.

Three miles from Beverley, the grand whitewashed house sits idyllically in the East Yorkshire countryside. All of its 20 ensuite bedrooms are individually furnished with regard to their Georgian heritage.

The Champagne Restaurant is one of only a handful in the county to hold the AA two Rosette award for cuisine with chef David Nowell's flagship menu being the champagne dinner, which is changed four times a year to make the most of seasonal produce. "Using quality local produce has always been important to Tickton Grange, even before it became fashionable," said David.

There are also three impressive function rooms for conferences and special occasions: the intimate and richly decorated Broadley Room, which seats just 20, the Garden Room with French windows opening onto a terrace, and the Rose Room catering for 180 guests.

Managing director Paul Whymant, who worked with his parents to create the welcoming hotel, said: "In a world in which individual and personal service is becoming scarce, we aim to offer all our customers the individual attention they traditionally deserve."

www.ticktongrange.co.uk

(Contact details on page 144)

Malmaison, Leeds

Once a bus depot office, the Malmaison hotel in Leeds is the perfect stop for a luxury weekend, a business stopover or a city break.

It's definitely a place for those who enjoy the finer things in life – like a room fully-equipped with everything you might need and tastefully decorated to the level of opulence. Rich, warm tones of aubergine and plum combine with subtle taupes to create a calm – and ever so slightly sultry – atmosphere, while velvet cushions with floor to ceiling windows help enhance the mood.

All rooms have the complete set of Mal ingredients – great beds, moody lighting, power showers, CD players, CD libraries, satellite TV, serious wines and naughty nibbles. Other little luxuries include fast and free internet access, same-day laundry, toiletries that guests are encouraged to take, and a 'vroom' room service for breakfast, dinner or midnight munchies.

The brasserie offers a locally-sourced 'home grown and local' menu and there are daringly good cocktails to be had at the bars. Malmaison CEO Robert B. Cook said: "Mal has some fantastic offers in order that local fans can still enjoy our hotels and brasseries as they always have in these tough times. More than ever, our good value philosophy shines through."

www.malmaison.com

(Contact details on page 186)

"The brasserie offers a locally-sourced 'home grown and local' menu and there are daringly good cocktails to be had at the bars"

Warm welcome

Here are some great ideas for places to stay:

City Chic:

Hotel du Vin, York – located on the tranquil area known as 'The Mount', Hotel du Vin York is a beautiful Grade II listed building that dates back to the early 19th century. With the HDV trademark bistro, bar and two private dining rooms, along with a courtyard for alfresco dining during the warmer months, it's a real treat.

Coastal:

The Crown Spa Hotel – on Scarborough's South Cliff Esplanade offers 160 years of service and a reputation for high standards and great sea views. Enjoy the heated pool or discover the new spa facilities this four-star hotel now offers.

Countryside Luxury:

Austwick Traddock , Austwick – a country house hotel situated within two acres of private landscaped gardens, it's an ideal location for visiting the Yorkshire Dales, Southern Lakes and Lancashire. Relax around open log fires and enjoy the hotel's peaceful and informal atmosphere. The Traddock's AA rosette restaurant has a menu that draws on many sources, accompanied in season with fresh herbs, fruit and vegetables from a local organic nursery.

Luxury with a difference:

Brompton Lakes, Richmond – enjoy a five-star luxury self-catering break and do as much or as little as you choose. Relax in stylish lodges and experience this quiet rural sanctuary.

Luxury guest accommodation:

17 Burgate, Pickering – renovated townhouse midway between the Market Place and the Castle in one of the region's most attractive and conveniently situated market towns. Modern facilities and amenities with traditional values and outstanding customer service – relax and indulge yourself.

Where to visit

Yorkshire is a wonderfully diverse region offering romantic moorland, pretty villages, lively cities and grand coastlines, making it the perfect place to plan your next break. Experience the lush valleys of the Yorkshire Dales, the huge skies and heather uplands of the North York Moors and the rugged landscapes of the Yorkshire Peak District, not forgetting the tranquil beauty of the Yorkshire Wolds.

Discover five lively, vibrant cities, all with their own distinct personalities. A sparkling array of theatres and award-winning restaurants, stunning attractions, a multi-cultural heritage, exciting architecture and shops galore.

Find the secluded coves, sandy beaches and pretty fishing villages along more than 100 miles of the amazingly varied Yorkshire coastline.

Literature comes alive; art and architecture hold your gaze; and melas, festivals, music and theatre provide non-stop entertainment.

For fine dining Yorkshire delivers. You will discover Michelin-starred eateries and no end of fine restaurants serving contemporary dishes from around the world. And the field-fresh, locally-sourced produce is second to none. Indeed Yorkshire prides itself on growing the finest ingredients and this has, in turn, attracted the finest chefs. And you'll be sure to taste the difference wherever you sit down to dine.

For more inspiration visit
www.yorkshire.com

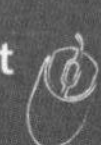

Explore and discover

NRM National Railway Museum

Where else would you get the chance to explore 300 years of railway history but at the NRM, York.

The museum is home to the nation's favourite locomotive, the Flying Scotsman and while she is currently undergoing a full restoration at sites around the country, visitors may be lucky enough to catch a glimpse of the restoration work in the workshop.

In the Great Hall you can marvel at the record-breaking Mallard – the fastest steam train in the world – take a seat on the futuristic Bullet Train, see a replica of Stephenson's Rocket, or step aboard the footplate of the Chinese locomotive, the largest in the NRM's collection.

Younger visitors can let off steam in a railway themed outdoor play area while railway fans can explore an open store of more than 750,000 objects covering every aspect of railway history.

Keeping the engines stoked is also part of the experience at NRM where hot meals and light snacks are taken in the Brief Encounter licensed restaurant and café on a railway platform, and delicious sandwiches, wraps, cakes, pastries and freshly brewed coffee are available from the Signal Box café in the Great Hall.

Entry to the museum is free, though there may be charges for special events.

www.nrm.org.uk

(Contact details on page 115)

"In the Great Hall you can marvel at the record-breaking Mallard – the fastest steam train in the world"

Pictures supplied by btpl Andrew Butler

Fountains Abbey

Situated in an area of outstanding natural beauty in the valley of the River Skell, Fountains Abbey and Studley Royal is Yorkshire's first World Heritage Site.

The huge estate – a National Trust property – offers a great and full family day out being home to the largest abbey ruins in the country and one of England's most spectacular Georgian water gardens.

Explore more than 800 acres of beautiful countryside and 10 historic buildings covering 800 years of history.

Year round there are activities for families, interesting walks and guided tours, and some fantastic evening events including open air theatre.

Fountains is a great place for a picnic, but for a mouth-watering alternative try the food on offer at its visitor centre restaurant which uses locally grown, seasonal and sustainably produced food wherever possible.

A committed supporter of local suppliers, Fountains' ingredients are also free from genetically modified organisms. Its eggs are free range as is its venison which is straight from the estate.

Open daily from 10am, the licensed restaurant serves morning coffee, light snacks, hot lunches and afternoon tea. You'll be tempted by the fresh seasonal home-made soup – a best seller – and the tasty home-made cakes, biscuits and sweet or savoury scones. Or stop by at the Studley Tearoom with its magnificent views over Studley Lake. Relax with a pot of tea – or keep it simple and go for a delicious Yorkshire ice-cream!

www.fountainsabbey.org.uk
(Contact details on page 93)

Yorkshire Wildlife Park

The Yorkshire Wildlife Park at Branton, Doncaster is Yorkshire's most exciting new attraction, offering visitors a chance to walk through natural habitats and encounter animals from all over the world.

The vision of the park, officially opened in April 2009, is to become a dynamic conservation centre, working with communities, conservationists and educators at home and abroad to help save habitats and wildlife.

At World's Farm, visitors can meet goats, sheep and other animals from farms around the globe, while younger visitors will love to catch feeding time on the friendly wallaby walkabout.

The park is home to the painted hunting dog, the rarest carnivore in Africa, and to antelopes, zebra, ostrich and ankole cattle – all roaming together on the 'African plains', while three species of endearing Madagascan primates are masters of the trees in Lemur Woods.

A Taste of Yorkshire is offered in the park's cafe of the same name, which provides a range of light snacks and traditional hot meals using regional produce, such as roast beef and Yorkshire puddings. Groups can book ahead for morning coffee with Yorkshire cakes and bakes, lunch or afternoon tea.

www.yorkshirewildlifepark.co.uk

(Contact details on page 156)

Royal Armouries

The Royal Armouries museum in Leeds houses a large part of the national collection of arms and armour in a multi-million pound purpose-built building a short distance from the city centre at Clarence Dock.

More than 8,500 objects are displayed throughout its five themed galleries – war, tournament, oriental, self-defence and hunting – plus the impressive Hall of Steel has a mass display of over 2,500 objects.

Between galleries, there are several opportunities for refreshment. The waterfront Nelson Bistro offers fresh coffee, home-made cakes and pastries and a hearty restaurant style lunch, plus there is a coffee shop on the second floor and a picnic area on floor four where you can eat your own packed lunch.

The museum also brings the past to life with lavish re-enactments – including real jousting with knights in armour – films and unique handling collections, making it popular with visitors of all ages and interests, whatever the weather.

Entry to the museum is free, but some events may be chargeable.

www.royalarmouries.org
(Contact details on page 188)

"More than 8,500 objects are displayed throughout its five themed galleries – war, tournament, oriental, self-defence and hunting – plus the impressive Hall of Steel has a mass display of over 2,500 objects"

“Buying British, buying locally and buying directly from farmers can all help make a difference in terms of improving our economy, sustainability and food security”

Dr John Sentamu, Archbishop of York

Source it

The following pages of this deliciouslyyorkshire Guide provide a comprehensive directory of Regional Food Group members: who they are, what they offer and where to find them. The directory is split by sub-region and category – producer, retailer, hospitality – to make it easier to find who and what you're looking for. Members are also listed according to their speciality: from bakers and confectioners and dairy and eggs to hotels and restaurants and outside caterers. And there's a quick, useful alphabetical index starting on page 214. Happy – and delicious – sourcing!

For more inspiration visit www.deliciouslyorkshire.co.uk

deliciouslyorkshire award winner 2008-09

Internet Sales

Mail Order

Own Retail Outlets

On Site Cafe / Restaurant

Children's Play Area

Site Tours / Demonstrations

North Yorkshire

Famed for its Gothic Minster, historic York is one of the UK's top award-winning cities, packed with contemporary shops, restaurants and attractions and exciting events all year long.

Further afield, Herriot Country is an area of grand sweeping hills, rich valleys, charming market towns and pretty villages.

If you're seeking a completely different experience every day, plan your break in the North York Moors where you can visit stately homes, enjoy the great outdoors, follow in the footsteps of tv and film heroes or experience a traditional agricultural show.

Further into North Yorkshire, Harrogate's cosmopolitan charm and character owes much to its heritage as a popular Victorian spa town with its famous Turkish Baths. Modern Harrogate is a lively mixture of fabulous shopping, café culture, fine restaurants and plenty of green open spaces.

Nearby, lies 680 square miles of Yorkshire Dales National Park and 233 square miles of the Nidderdale Area of Outstanding Natural Beauty, both prime locations for outdoor adventures. And North Yorkshire is home to a wealth of beer and cheese producers. You can enjoy a range of local produce, whether it be served in Michelin-starred eateries or sold to you direct at farmers markets.

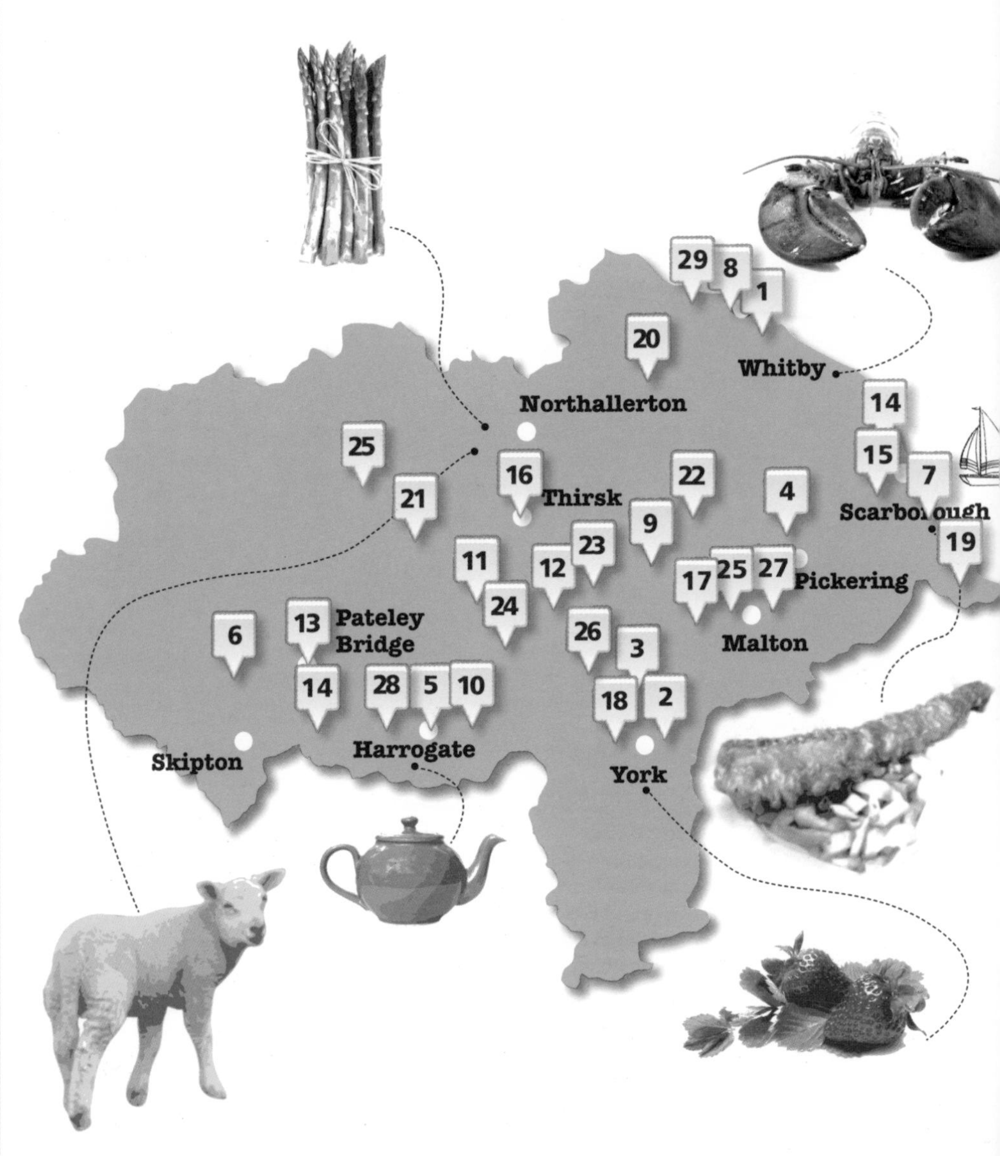
29
8
1
20
Whitby
Northallerton
14
25
16
22
15
7
21
Thirsk
4
Scarborough
9
19
23
11
12
17
25
27
Pickering
24
13
Pateley Bridge
6
26
Malton
3
14
28
5
10
18
2
Skipton
Harrogate
York

Food Highlights

Bakers & confectioners

Angel Chocolates

Award winning hand-made chocolate products including our original bags of hand-cut slabs in more than 20 flavours. All made with Valrhona chocolate – the best chocolate this side of heaven.

Details

Leigh Torrance
01748 884374
The Hayloft
1C Silver Street
Reeth, Richmond
DL11 6SP North Yorkshire
E: **angel@swaledale.org**
W: **www.angelchocolates.co.uk**

Did you know?

488,000

There are 488,000 pigs in the county – nearly two thirds of the English total.

Bakers & confectioners

E. Botham & Sons Ltd

Family run craft bakers and confectioners in Whitby since 1865. Selling a wide range of wrapped goods for wholesale nationally and internationally. Also worldwide mail-order and award winning tearooms.

Details

Mike Jarman
01947 602823
35/39 Skinner Street
Whitby
YO21 3AH
North Yorkshire
F: **01947 820269**
E: **sales@botham.co.uk**
W: **www.botham.co.uk**

Bakers & confectioners

Choc-Affair

Here at Choc-Affair we believe that chocolate should be an experience, not just a treat, and we are committed to producing a wonderfully delicious, ethically made range of Fairtrade chocolate indulgences. We supply delis, farm shops, hotels, cafés and hamper companies. Make a difference: choose Fairtrade.

Details

Linda Barrie
01904 541541
Marina House
York Road
Naburn York
YO19 4RW
North Yorkshire
F: **01904 541541**
E: **linda@choc-affair.com**
W: **www.chocaffair.com**

akers & confectioners

The Chocolate Factory Ltd

The Chocolate Factory produces fresh handmade chocolates, handmade chocolate figures and a full range of diabetic chocolate. Everything made by hand with real Belgian chocolate. Watch the chocolatiers in action at The Chocolate Factory in Hutton Le Hole on the edge of the Yorkshire Moors.

Details

Gareth East
01751 477469
Unit 2
Hutton le Hole
YO62 6UA
North Yorkshire
W: **www.the-chocolate-factory.co.uk**

Bakers & confectioners

Confectionery Craft Ltd

Confectionery Craft, trading under the Parrs brand name, manufactures a range of traditional sugar confectionery products including fruit jellies, lollipops, cinder toffee and rock.

Details

John Grimshaw
01636 706163
The Sweet Factory
23 - 25 Sherwood Street
Scarborough YO11 1SR
North Yorkshire
F: **01723 352967**
E: **john@grimshawcc.fsnet.co.uk**

Did you know?

The Yorkshire and Humber food and drink sector is the most diverse in the country

Bakers & confectioners

Country Fare

Winner of 21 Great Taste Awards, you really can be assured of the quality of all of our products. The cakes are made by hand, using free range eggs, local milk and butter. All our cakes are made from family recipes in our artisan bakery on our working hill farm.

Details

Dianne Halliday
01768 371173
Dalefoot Farm
Mallerstang
Kirkby Stephen
CA17 4JT
North Yorkshire
F: **01768 371173**
E: **countryfareuk@aol.com**
W: **www.country-fare.co.uk**

Bakers & confectioners

Davill's Patisserie

An accredited and award winning Independent Master Baker based in the market City of Ripon. Produces a variety of fresh breads, delicious cakes, coverture chocolates and Easter items. Specialises in good 'Yorkshire fayre' including Yorkshire curd tarts, Fat Rascals and Yorkshire parkin. Suppliers to retailers, hotels, markets and shows.

Details
Ken Davill
01765 603544
24 Westgate
Ripon
HG4 2BQ
North Yorkshire
E: **kenandshirleydavill@hotmail.com**

Bakers & confectioners

Eminence Cakes of Distinction

Say it with Cakes! Eminence produce a delicious range of homemade cakes and confectionery gifts, delivering direct to your door. Bespoke celebration cakes also available. Why not visit our website?

Details
Emma Townend
01757 291391
5 Beech Croft
Barlby, Selby
YO8 5UY North Yorkshire
E: **emma@eminencecakes.co.uk**

Farrahs Harrogate Toffee

Bakers and confectioners. Farrah's toffee is cooked slowly in open copper kettles in small batches and stirred by hand. Old fashioned toffee.

Details
Peter Marston
01423 883000
Pennine Range Mills
Camwal Road
Starbeck, Harrogate
HG1 4PY
North Yorkshire
F: **01423 883029**
E: **sales@farrahs.com**

Bakers & confectioners

Gingerbread House

We produce a range of gingerbread biscuits in various shapes and sizes. Flat pack DIY Gingerbread House Kits available on line. Gingerbread houses of different sizes workshops and childrens parties.

Details
Liz Druce
01845 537133
Pen Hill Cottage
Kepwick
Thirsk
YO7 2JW
E: **lizdruce@tiscali.co.uk**

The Gluten Free Kitchen

Award-winning bakery producing gluten, wheat and dairy-free cakes, puddings and savouries. Our products are also additive and preservative free. However, what they have in abundance is a delicious taste! Joint winner Foods Matter 2009 Free From Awards - Cakes, Muffins & Sweet Biscuits category.

Details
Sue Powell
01969 666999
The Gluten Free Kitchen
Wensleydale Business Park
Hawes
North Yorkshire
DL8 3UZ
F: **01969 666999**
E: **info@theglutenfreekitchen.co.uk**
W: **www.theglutenfreekitchen.co.uk**

Bakers & confectioners

GSN Cakes & Chocolates

Bespoke hand crafted, unique chocolate wedding cakes and chocolates. Available in French, Swiss, Belgian, milk, dark or white chocolate special occasion cup-cakes. Hand crafted chocolate deities, dragons and roses – stunning in detail as they are in flavour.

Details

Gywnn Nicholls
07939 899719
39 Albemarle Road
York
YO23 1EP
North Yorkshire
E: **gwynn923@btinternet.com**

Bakers & confectioners

It's Nut Free

Manufacturer and contract packer of cakes, cereal bars, snack bags and chocolate – all in our purpose-built, nut-free factory. Supply to education and health sectors, all major retailers, fine food delis, coffee shops, farm shops, export and mail order.

Details

Angela Russell
01609 775660
Moxon Court
Northallerton
DL6 2NG
North Yorkshire
F: **08452 802713**
E: **sales@itsnutfree.com**
E: **info@itsnutfree.com**
W: **www.itsnutfree.com**

Bakers & confectioners

Jim Garrahy's Fudge Kitchen Ltd

Our shop in York has been handmaking fudge to a traditional 1830s recipe for 25 years, using all natural ingredients in front of the customer. Freshly produced in thick slabs in 20+ flavours it is also available by mail-order, for unique wedding and corporate favours and now for wholesale.

Details

Jack Wilkinson
01904 645596
58 Low Petergate
York
YO1 ZHZ
North Yorkshire
E: **york@fudgekitchen.co.uk**
W: **www.fudgekitchen.co.uk**

Bakers & confectioners

Just Puds Ltd

A deliciously naughty experience for all pudding lovers, skilfully crafted from our favourite recipes. We're proud to make our puds from only the finest ingredients, sourced locally wherever we can. Serve with cream, ice cream or simply on its own, and indulge yourself in pure pud pleasure.

Details

Graeme Robinson
0845 4097009
Lamb Hill Farm
Masham
Ripon
HG4 4DJ
North Yorkshire
F: **0845 4097008**
E: **rosemary@justpuds.co.uk**
W: **www.justpuds.co.uk**

Bakers & confectioners

The Little Chocolate Shop Ltd

The Little Chocolate Shop is a unique attraction in the picturesque Yorkshire Dales. Our bespoke factory includes a gift shop, a viewing area for you to watch delicious handmade chocolates and confectionery being hand crafted, and a demonstration area where you can learn about the fascinating world of chocolate.

Details

Clare Gardiner
01969 625288
Leyburn Business Park
Harmby Road
Leyburn
DL8 5QA
North Yorkshire
F: **01969 625027**
W: **www.thelittlechocolate shop.co.uk**

Bakers & confectioners

Leyburn Bakery & Deli

Traditional bakery selling a range of speciality breads, cakes and more. We use local organic flour and ingredients and hand bake everything in Leyburn in our artisan bakery. Trade enquiries are very welcome.

Details

Paula Richardson
01969 625619
Unit 1, Central Building
Market Place, Leyburn
DL8 5RD
North Yorkshire
E: **bread@leyburnbakery.co.uk**

M.A. Worsdale

A small local business providing traditional handmade cakes, scones and biscuits from locally sourced fresh ingredients at farmers markets, farmshops and regional shows.

Details

Mabel Worsdale
01677 450276
Low Hall Farm, Hunton
Bedale DL8 1QF
North Yorkshire
E: **lizworsdale@aol.com**

Stickylicious

roducers of scrumptious and-made cakes, tray bakes nd award winning luxury ruit cakes, lovingly baked in ur farmhouse Aga to tantalise our taste buds. Using ocally sourced ingredients vhere possible.

Details
Carolyn Chapman
01677 450202
Hessleton Farm, Hunton
Bedale DL8 1LU
North Yorkshire
F: **01677 450202**
E: **stickylicious@hotmail.co.uk**

J Stringer & Sons

J Stringer & Sons is a family un farm on the Yorkshire Wolds. Our flours, bread mixes and breakfast foods are produced from organic cereals grown and milled on our farm. deliciouslyorkshire award winner.

Details
Lisa Cardy
01759 369859
High Callis Wold
Bishop Wilton
York YO42 1TD
North Yorkshire
F: **01759 368221**
E: **highcalliswold@aol.com**
W: **www.localfoodshop.co.uk**

Taste of Yorkshire

We supply high quality, handmade savoury biscuits and Fat Betty nibbles. We also sell mail order Christmas hampers nationally.

Details
Jonathan Kidd
01423 359919
5 Centre Park, Marston
Business Park, Tockwith
YO26 7QF North Yorkshire
F: **01423 359919**
E: **kidd@cheeseco.demon.co.uk**
W: **www.tasteofyorkshire.co.uk**

Velvet Heaven

Velvet confectionery will be producing excellent confectionery specializing in fudges and will be supplying not only restaurants and shops but retailing at the Station in Richmond.

Details
Jane Gallogly
01748 825340
Station Buildings
Station Yard, Richmond
DL10 4LD North Yorkshire
E: **jane@restaurant-seasons.co.uk**

Woodheads Scarborough Ltd

The Pie People are a family owned bakery business based in Yorkshire and have been baking pies for over 60 years, using the finest quality ingredients, the best recipes and of course the most experienced craft bakers who make it happen.
Pies for retail, business to business and foodservice nationwide.

Details
Philip Davis
01723 363561
Beaconsfield Street
Scarborough
YO12 4EL
North Yorkshire
F: **01723 501096**
E: **phildavis7@btconnect.com**
W: **www.thepiepeople.com**

Bakers & confectioners

Yorkshire Dales Granola

Produced by Yockenthwaite Farm, Yorkshire Dales Granola is a delicious wholegrain cereal made from spelt, wheat, oats and other natural ingredients. Based on a traditional recipe, granola can be eaten for breakfast as a dessert or snack.

Details

Elizabeth & Stuart Hird
01756 760835
Yockenthwaite Farm,
Buckden
Skipton
BD23 5JH
North Yorkshire
W: **www.yorkshiredalesgranola.co.uk**
E: **info@yorkshiredalesgranola.co.uk**

Beverages (alcoholic & non)

Ampleforth Abbey Orchards

Our orchard, said to be the most Northern commercial orchard in England, situated in the magnificent Howardian hills has supplied apples to the local population for over 100 years. The Ampleforth monks make a variety of products including our delicious cider.

Details

Rainer Verbourg
01439 766825
The Orchard, Ampleforth, York, YO62 4EN North Yorkshire
E: **rainer@ampleforth.org.uk**

Beverages (alcoholic & non)

Black Sheep Brewery

The Black Sheep Brewery visitor centre offers shepherded tours around the brewhouse and fermenting room. Guests can experience the brewing processes and sample our award-winning ales at the Baa...r. The bistro provides locally sourced culinary delights and the sheepy shop is full of ewe-nique gifts.

Details

Louise Guy
01765 689227
Wellgarth
Masham
Ripon
HG4 4EN
North Yorkshire
F: **01765 689746**
W: **www.blacksheepbrewery.co.uk**

Beverages (alcoholic & non)

Hambleton Ales

Brewers of real ale and bottlers of the finest quality premium ales from the heart of Yorkshire available in pubs, off licences, supermarkets and restaurants all over the UK. Also the leading British brewed gluten free ale and lager in the world.

Details

Nick Stafford
01765 640108
The Brewery
Melmerby Green Road
Melmerby, Ripon
HG4 5NB
North Yorkshire
W: **www.hambletonales.co.uk**

The New Inn & Cropton Brewery

Set in beautiful Yorkshire Dales providing accommodation for the traveller since 1776. Lovingly and carefully refurbished. You will experience a warm and friendly welcome.

Details

Pauline Pilkington
01751 417330
Woolcroft
Cropton
Nr Pickering
YO18 8HH
North Yorkshire
F: **01751 417582**
E: **info@croptonbrewery.co.uk**
W: **www.croptonbrewery.com**

Beverages (alcoholic & non)

Raisthorpe Manor Fine Foods

With a country heritage, Raisthorpe Manor Fine Foods use only the best ingredients combined with traditional methods to ensure our products are of the highest quality. We provide the finest quality liqueurs, preserves and chocolates with an emphasis on great taste combined with a reliable and friendly service.

Details

Julia Medforth
01377 288295
Raisthorpe Manor
Thixendale
York YO17 9TF
North Yorkshire
E: **enquiries@raisthorpemanor.com**
W: **www.raisthorpemanor.com**

Beverages (alcoholic & non)

Richmond Brewing Company Limited

The Richmond Brewing Company is a microbrewery situated in The Station in Richmond. Supplying bottle and cask beers to both Station visitors and business customers around Richmond and the Yorkshire area.

Details

Andrew Hamilton
01748 828266
Richmond DL10 4LD
North Yorkshire
E: **andy@richmondbrewing.co.uk**
W: **www.richmondbrewing.co.uk**

Did you know?

1,139,348

There are 1,139,348 lambs in Yorkshire (over a seventh of the English total)

Beverages (alcoholic & non)

Sloe Motion

Sloe Motion is based on Green Farm near York. Our sloe gin (Gold Star, Great Taste Awards 08) brandy, whisky and vodka are produced in the traditional way using high concentrations of fruit to ensure a fabulous flavour. We then use the infused sloes in our unique chocolate truffles (deliciouslyyorkshire award winner 08-9) and chutney.

Details

Jonathan Curtoys
0844 8001911
Green Farm
Barton Le Willows
York
YO60 7PD
North Yorkshire
F: **01653 618313**
W: **www.sloemotion.com**

Beverages (alcoholic & non)

Thorncroft Ltd

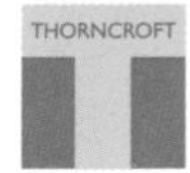

National Trust sites, farm shops, delis, garden centres, and consumer shows throughout Yorkshire – that's where to look for Thorncroft's unique range of botanical cordials and sparkling drinks. New for 2009 – Healthy Thirst sparkling drinks are now made with no added sugar and are free from any preservatives or artificial sweeteners.

Details

Michael Haigh
01642 791792
Sowerby Way
Durham Lane Industrial Park
Eaglescliffe Stockton-on-Tees
Middlesbrough
TS16 0RB
F: **01642 791793**
E: **info@thorncroftdrinks.co.uk**
W: **www.thorncroftdrinks.co.uk**

Beverages (alcoholic & non)

Yorkshire Country Wines

We produce a range of quality country wines from fruits and flowers; including elderberry, elderflower, gooseberry, blackberry and damson – each variety has its own distinctive character and flavour. Idyllically located tearoom overlooking the River Nidd.

Details

Richard Brown
01423 711947
The Riverside Cellars, The Mill, Glasshouses, Harrogate
HG3 5QH North Yorkshire
F: **01423 711947**
E: **info@yorkshirecountrywines.co.uk**
W: **www.yorkshirecountrywines.co.uk**

Yorkshire Wolds Apples

Traditional apple juice farm-pressed in East Yorkshire. The apples we press produce a sugar free healthy and juice that contains no additives and is a perfect addition to your healthy 5 a day.

Details

Ray Kirby
07531 597267
28 Springdale Road
Market Weighton YO43 3JT
North Yorkshire
E: **rayk@mktw.karoo.co.uk**
W: **www.yorkshirewoldapplejuice.co.uk**

Acorn Dairy

corn Dairy processes and istributes organic milk, ream and butter produced vith milk from their herd. ecognised for excellent service nd organic milk in the region, upplying doorsteps, retail nd wholesalers.

)etails
:aroline Tweddle
)1325 466999
rchdeacon Newton
)arlington DL2 2YB
lorth Yorkshire
': **01325 464567**
:: **organic@acorndairy.co.uk**
/: **www.acorndairy.co.uk**

Birchfield Family Dairies and Farmshop

raditional dairy ice cream made rom milk and cream produced y a herd of pedigree jerseys. lso produce flavoured butters. lewly opened farm shop.

)etails
/lartin Whitley
)113 2037733
irchfield Farm
ummerbridge, Harrogate
IG3 4JS North Yorkshire
:: **birchfieldicecream@live.co.uk**

Beacon Farm Ice Cream

We make traditional dairy ice cream and luxury sorbets in a variety of flavours. Supplying to the retail and catering trade, alongside our ice cream parlour and tearooms here on the farm.

Details
Michael Shardlow
01947 605212
Beacon Farm
Beacon Way
Sneaton
YO22 5HS
North Yorkshire
F: **01947 604670**
W: **www.beaconfarmicecream.co.uk**

Brymor Ice Cream Ltd

Producing 32 different flavours of award winning ice cream, using our own milk from the pedigree Guernsey herd. On-site ice cream parlour with 250,000 visitors per annum.

Details
Robert Moore
01677 460377
High Jervaulx Farm, Masham
Ripon HG4 4PG
North Yorkshire
F: **01677 460345**
E: **nicola@brymordairy.co.uk**
W: **www.brymordairy.co.uk**

Laceys Cheese Ltd

At Laceys Cheese we take great pride in our craft to bring you a high quality, locally produced product. Come on down to The Station to see how traditional cheeses are made.

Details
Simon Lacey
01748 828264
Unit 1, Station Buildings
Richmond DL10 4LD
North Yorkshire
F: **01748 828264**
E: **enquiries@laceyscheese.co.uk**
W: **www.laceyscheese.co.uk**

Dairy & Eggs

Paynes Dairy

Paynes Dairies Ltd is one of the largest independent dairies in the UK. We trade across all sectors including maunufacturing, retail, foodservice and independents. We pride ourselves on quality and service, producing a full range of fresh milk and creams in all pack sizes.

Details

Kevin Leech
01423 326058
Bar Lane
Boroughbridge
York
YO51 9LU
North Yorkshire
E: **sales@paynesdairies.co.uk**
W: **www.paynesdairies.com**

The Ribblesdale Cheese Company

Artisan cheese maker and wholesaler, using local goat and ewes' milk. All of our cheese is hand waxed and we smoke our own cheese over oak chippings. Grade A BRC quality accreditation.

Details

Iona Hill
01969 667788
Upper Wensleydale Business Park, Brunt Acres Road
Hawes DL8 3UZ
North Yorkshire
E: **ionahill@gmail.com**
W: **www.yorkshiredalescheese.co.uk**

Did you know?

There are 84 breweries in the historic county of Yorkshire, the oldest of which is Samuel Smith's Old Brewery at Tadcaster, founded in 1758.

Dairy & Eggs

Ripley Store

Our world famous delicious creamy, tasty ice cream has been made for decades to a well kept secret recipe. With a different flavour to choose ever week it will keep you coming back time and time again. Quit possibly the best ice cream you will ever taste!

Details

David Thomson
01423 770044
Beechwood
Ripley
Harrogate
HG3 3AX
North Yorkshire
E: **info@ripleyicecream.com**

Ryeburn of Helmsley

Ryeburn of Helmsley has been producing delicious award winning dairy ice cream and sorbet for 21 years. We have one of the largest selections of flavours in the country. We are very much a family run firm who enjoyed recognition of the quality of our products.

Details

David Otterburn
01439 770331
Church Farm
Cleveland Way, Helmsley
YO62 5AT North Yorkshire
E: **info@ryeburn.com**
W: **www.ryeburn.com**

Dairy & Eggs

Shepherds Purse Cheeses Ltd

Shepherds Purse produce artisan multi-award winning cheeses in our BRC higher level accredited dairy using cows, ewes and water buffalo milk. Our brands include Yorkshire Blue, Mrs Bells Blue, Buffalo Blue, Byland Blue, Fine Fettle, Basilano, Katy's White Lavender and the Ryedale Range.

Details

Judy & Katie Bell
01845 587220
Leachfield Grange
Newsham
Thirsk
YO7 4DJ
North Yorkshire
F: **01845 587717**
E: **info@shepherdspurse.co.uk**
W: **www.shepherdspurse.co.uk**

Dairy & Eggs

Stamfrey Farm Organics

Award winning organic clotted cream and yoghurt, handmade on our own dairy farm using traditional methods. Suppliers to some of the finest cafes and restaurants in Yorkshire – also available in selected farm shops and delis.

Details

Sue Gaudie
01609 882297
Stamfrey Farm, West Rounton
Northallerton DL6 2LJ
North Yorkshire
F: **01609 882297**
E: **info@stamfrey.co.uk**
W: **www.stamfrey.co.uk**

Swales Yorkshire Dales Ice Cream

Not only do we manufacture Yorkshire Dales Ice Cream here on the farm, we also retail it; from our own fleet of vans and from summer 2009, our fabulous new ice cream parlour here at the farm.

Details

Mandy Rogers
01756 710685
Calm Slate Farm Halton East,
Skipton BD23 6EJ
North Yorkshire
F: **01756 710345**
W: **www.yorkshiredalesicecream.co.uk**

Dairy & Eggs

Swaledale Cheese Company

A family run business set in the heart of the Yorkshire Dales making award winning, artisan Swaledale Cheeses. Our range of 14 cheeses includes goat, sheep and cow varieties. We hold PDO status on both the traditional cows and sheeps cheese varieties.

Details

Mandy Reed
01748 824932
Mercury Road
Gallowfields
Richmond
DL10 4TQ
North Yorkshire
F: **01748 822219**
E: **sales@swaledalecheese.co.uk**
W: **www.swaledalecheese.co.uk**

Wensleydale Dairy Products Ltd

As the only makers of Real Yorkshire Wensleydale Cheese in the world, we are proud to achieve global acclaim for our award winning cheeses.

Details
David Hartley
01969 667664
Gayle Lane
Hawes
DL8 3RN
North Yorkshire
E: **creamery@wensleydale.co.uk**
W: **www.wensleydale.co.uk**

Yoghurt Delights

Deliciouslyorkshire and deliciously low fat. The healthy alternative to ice cream. Each frozen yoghurt is made using live yoghurt cultures. Why not come and try some at the region's shows and events?

Details
Elaine Newham
01723 870048
Highlands Farm
Lindhead Road, Burniston
Scarborough YO13 0DL
North Yorkshire
F: **01723 871461**

Yorkshire Farmhouse Eggs Ltd

A family business that has been producing and packing the finest quality free range and organic eggs for 25 years. BEIC Lion quality, RSPCA freedom foods, BRC, Soil Association, Organic Farmers & Growers and Vegetarian Society approved.

Details

James Potter
01845 578376
Village Farm
Catton
Thirsk
YO7 4SQ
North Yorkshire
F: **01845 578660**
W: **www.yorkshirefarmhouse.co.uk**

iry & Eggs

Yorvale Ltd

Traditional methods and the finest ingredients produce rich and creamy dairy ice cream from our family farm in the Vale of York. We combine the milk with double cream and use only natural ingredients, flavourings and colourings to create ice cream that tastes divine.
5 litre, 2 litre, 500ml and 120ml

Details

Lesley Buxton
01904 706702
Fossfield Farm
Acaster Malbis
York
YO23 2XA
North Yorkshire
F: **01904 702378**
E: **icecream@yorvale.co.uk**
W: **www.icecream@yorvale.co.uk**

Fish (Fresh & smoked)

Carricks Fish Ltd

Carricks Fish Ltd is a family run business specialising in traditional and natural smoked fish, fresh fish, fresh fruit and vegetables and delicatessen.

Details

Chris Revis
01677 470261
Yew Tree House
Snape
Bedale
DL8 2TJ
North Yorkshire
E: **carricks-ltd@btconnect.com**

Did you know?

The Great Yorkshire Show goes back 171 years. It used to tour 30 towns before the innovative decision was made in 1950 to build a permanent showground in Harrogate.

Fish (fresh & smoked)

Whitby Seafish Ltd

WHITBY SEAFISH LTD

Suppliers of fresh, hand-prepared fish from Whitby and Scarborough. We can help you meet the needs of an increasingly demanding consumer who wants to try new tastes but is concerned about 'food miles', sustainability and traceability. There is a huge variety of fresh fish and seafood available from Whitby and Scarborough markets, and of course our own smoked fish.

Details

Matthew Asquith
01947 841236
Unit 1a Whitegate Close
Saltburn
Staithes
TS13 5BB
North Yorkshire
F: **01947 841236**
E: **whitby-seafish@btconnect.com**
W: **www.whitbyseafish.co.uk**

Fresh Ingredients

Herbs Unlimited

We grow fresh cut herbs, baby salads, spinach and washed ready to eat lettuce mixes, all freshly picked from our farm in Yorkshire in the summer and imported from highly reputable companies in the winter. We specialise in unusual herbs , giving you a point of difference and often inspiration.

Details

Alison Dodd
01845 587694
Hawker Lane
Sandhutton
Thirsk
YO7 4RW
North Yorkshire
F: **01845 587695**
E: **sglltd@btconnect.com**
W: **www.herbsunlimited.co.uk**

Fresh Ingredients

Stuarts Foods Ltd

A high quality, fresh food wholesaler based in Scarborough, specialising in fresh fruit and vegetables. Sourcing only the freshest and best quality ingredients for local and national customers in the foodservice, manufacturing and retail sectors. We are BRC accredited to grade A and have a modern fleet of refrigerated delivery vehicles.

Details

Damian Howarth
01723 582252
Howarth House
Dunslow Court
Eastfield
Scarborough
YO11 3XT
North Yorkshire
E: **info@stuartsfoods.co.uk**
W: **www.stuartsfoods.co.uk**

Ingredient Suppliers

Rafis Spicebox

Rafi's
Spicebox

Rafi's Spicebox specialise in preparing the unique 'Curry Pack', which was invented by our founder and author Rafi Fernandez. Choose from 27 varieties: spices, garlic, chillies and onions are carefully blended to your taste. Simple, no chopping and no oil. You can create an authentic curry in 25 minutes!

Details

Kevin Fernandez
01904 638119
17 Goodramgate
York
YO1 7LW
North Yorkshire
E: **york@spicebox.co.uk.**
W: **www.spicebox.co.uk**

Arthur Haigh Ltd

Arthur Haigh's are based at Dalton near Thirsk, in the centre of Herriot country. We are a second-generation family business, excelling in premium award winning cooked meats and champion pork sausage varieties. We dry cure our own high quality bacon and gammon. We are black pudding champions, winning awards both nationally and in Europe.

Details

Duncan Haigh
01845 578227
Feedemwell
Unit G Dalton Airfield
Industrial Estate
Dalton, Thirsk
YO7 3HE
North Yorkshire
F: **01845 578648**
W: **www.yorkshireblackpudding.co.uk**

Bare Earth

A taste of Africa made in Yorkshire – Bare Earth manufactures a range of meat products – using traditional Southern African recipes. Our core products – Biltong and Droewors are speciality meat snacks made from cured air dried beef whilst Boerewors a 100%

Details

Thomo Letaine
01765 641824
8 Hallikeld Close, Barker Business Park, Melmerby
HG4 5GZ North Yorkshire
F: **01765 640628**
E: **info@bare-earth.co.uk**

The Blue Pig Company

Family run business with free range, rare breed Gloucester Old Spots and Saddleback pigs in the Yorkshire Dales. We produce gourmet sausages, dry cured bacons, gammons, black pudding and pork – born, reared, prepared on our farm.

Details

Andrew Bradley
01729 840218
Mearbeck, Long Preston
Skipton BD23 4QP
North Yorkshire
E: **andrew@bluepigcompany.com**
W: **www.bluepigcompany.com**

Colin M Robinson

The premier retailer of Limestone Country traditionally bred beef. Home reared Rock View pork and lamb. Award winning homemade sausages and home dry cured bacon and ham. Homemade meat products and home cooked meats all prepared to the very highest of standards. We also have a shop based at The Mackenzies Smokehouse retail outlet in Blubberhouses, North Yorkshire – please refer to Mackenzies entry for address details.

Details

Colin Robinson
01756 752476
41 Main Street
Grassington
Skipton
BD23 5AA
North Yorkshire
F: **01756 753985**
W: **www.colinmrobinson.co.uk**

Meat, poultry & game (fresh & smoked)

Debbie & Andrews

Producers of quality sausages under the Debbie & Andrew's brand. Also produce dry cured bacon and hams. Supply supermarkets, delis etc. Manufacturing fresh, chilled and cooked frozen sausages on a national basis.

Details

Debbie Keeble
0800 7836481
Berryhills, Kirklington
Bedale
DL8 2NL
North Yorkshire
E: **debbie@debbieandandrews.co.uk**
www.debbieandandrews.co.uk

Farmhouse Direct

Farmers and producers of rare breed meats and sausages. Handmade rare breed pork pies with delicious toppings – Brandsby Pies which can be purchased at top class delis throughout Yorkshire.

Details

David & Jacqui Kitson
01347 889354
Farmhouse Direct
Seaves Farm, Brandsby, York
YO61 4RT North Yorkshire
E: **info@farmhousedirect.com**
W: **www.farmhousedirect.com**

Meat, poultry & game (fresh & smoked)

Holme Farmed Venison

Holme Farmed Venison provides the finest quality venison farmed to the highest standards in Yorkshire. Our deer are naturally reared on grass pastures guaranteeing a beautifully lean and tender red meat. We provide a wide range of cuts to restaurants, hotels, pubs, both large and small retailers and private customers.

Details

Fiona Campbell
01977 686440
9 First Avenue
Aviation Road
Sherburn in Elmet
Leeds
LS25 6PD
North Yorkshire
F: **01977 686441**
E: **info@hfv.co.uk**
W: **www.hfv.co.uk**

Meat, poultry & game (fresh & smoked)

Paganum

Paganum are producers and suppliers of quality, speciality meat and poultry products. Paganum is a family run farm and online farmers' market supplying restaurants, pubs and hotels and direct to the home all over the UK with free delivery. We are passionate about Yorkshire produce and quality food.

Details

Chris Wildman
01729 830727
Manor House
Kirkby Malham
Skipton
BD23 4BX
North Yorkshire
F: **01729 901051**
E: **chris@paganum.co.uk**
W: **www.paganum.co.uk**

eat, poultry & game (fresh & smoked)

Robinsons Pork Butchers Knaresborough Ltd

Robinsons is a well established family business in Knaresborough. We make handmade, award winning speciality pork pies and sausages. We are a traditional business with a modern twist.

Details

Mick Robinson
01423 863077
46 Market Place, Knaresborough
HG5 8AG North Yorkshire
E: **m.wrobinson@btopenworld.com**

Did you know?

The food and drink sector's annual contribution to the regional economy is worth £8 billion *(ONS 2008)*

Meat, poultry & game (fresh & smoked)

Seamer Fayre

Indulge your palate with the delicious flavours and succulent tenderness of home grown, matured Aberdeen Angus beef, Gloucester Old Spot pork and bacon, lamb and wild venison, reared extensively on the beautiful Yorkshire coast and prepared and sold in our own farm shop and butchery.

Details

Elaine Keith
01723 863600
Bridge Farm Main Street
Seamer
Scarborough
YO12 4PS
North Yorkshire
W: **www.seamerfayre.co.uk**

Meat, poultry & game (fresh & smoked)

Sykes House Farm Ltd

Sykes House Farm has a long established reputation as a leading supplier of top quality fresh meat and poultry to the catering industry. You can find our products in many of the top restuarants and catering establishments across the North of England. Deeply involved in the whole supply chain, we source only the best local produce.

Details

Robert Smith
01937 582549
Wetherby
LS23 7DR
North Yorkshire
F: **01937 582549**
E: **enquiries@sykeshousefarm.co.uk**
W: **www.syskeshousefarm.co.uk**

Meat, poultry & game (fresh & smoked)

Taste Tradition Ltd

Taste Tradition is a family run business producing and supplying the highest quality rare/native breed meat. Our pork, lamb and beef are served in some of the finest restaurants, stores and butchers nationwide. Our breeds include Gloucester Old Spot, Saddleback, Welsh Pork, Longhorn, Galloway and Dexter Beef, Swaledale and Suffolk Lamb. Specialities – suckling pig, porchetta and sausages.

Details

Joyce & Charles Ashbridge
01845 525330
Units I & J, Lumley Close
Thirsk Industrial Park
Thirsk
YO7 3TD
North Yorkshire
F: **01845 525331**
E: **joyce@tastetradition.co.uk**
W: **www.tastetradition.co.uk**

Meat, poultry & game (fresh & smoked)

Thornhill Dexter Beef

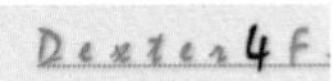

Top quality, award-winning beef from this well-known herd of Dexter Cattle, which graze meadows in the Vale of York. Natually reared on grass and hay, the beef has high Omega 3 content and is beautifully marbled with a rich flavour. Open Saturdays 10am – 4pm.

Details

Penny Hodgson
01347 823827
Thornhill Farm
Thirsk Road
Easingwold
YO61 3ND
North Yorkshire
F: **01347 823827**
E: **thornhillfarm@btinternet.com**
W: **www.dexter4foodies.com**

Meat, poultry & game (fresh & smoke

Trotters Farm Shop

We specialise in our own home reared free range pork. Our pigs have the freedom to root and roam, giving a traditional tasting pork. Fresh cuts of pork, award winning sausages, dry cured bacon and hams. Also a selection of locally reared beef, lamb and poultry, all cut to your specification.

Details

Paul Bradbury
01944 710721
Gladvic Farm
Potter Brompton
Scarborough
YO12 4PF
North Yorkshire
E: **info@trotterspork.com**
W: **www.trotterspork.com**

eat, poultry & game (fresh & smoked)

West Moor Meats

Family run pig farming business established for over 38 years. Farm butchery on site supplying customers with fresh meat.

Details

Jill Piercy
01347 824300
West Moor
Easingwold Road
Stillington
York
YO61 1LT
North Yorkshire
E: **jill.piercy@qnetadsl.com**

Whole Hog Sausage Co Ltd

Producing kitchen-made whole hog sausages of the highest quality. Made with all prime cuts from hand-boned animals reared in the Dales. Varieties are Original Toulouse Italian and Chorizo as well as special recipes to order.

Details

Peter Olley
01765 690680
Monkton Lodge
Main Street
Bishop Monkton
HG3 3QP
North Yorkshire

Meat, poultry & game (fresh & smoked)

Yorkshire Dales Meat Company Ltd

One of the largest catering butchers in Yorkshire supplying quality and well matured beef, pork, lamb, poultry and game to hotels, restaurants, gastro pubs and supermarkets. Also see us at farmers markets and food festivals.

Details

Stephen Knox
01748 810042
Mill Close Farm
Patrick Brompton, Bedale
DL8 1JY North Yorkshire
F: **01748 813612**
E: **info@yorkshiredalesmeat.com**
W: **www.yorkshiredalesmeat.com**

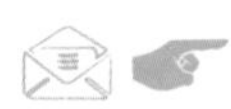

Did you know?

13%

More than 13% of all England's rapeseed oil is produced in the region

Meat, poultry & game (fresh & smoked)

Yorkshire Game Ltd

Yorkshire Game supplies fresh, oven ready game and specialist foods to the catering trade, operating from an EC export licensed plant in North Yorkshire. Wild Scottish venison, grouse, pheasant, partridge, wild duck, woodpigeon, hare and rabbit.

Details

Richard Townsend
01748 810212
Station Road Industrial Park
Brompton on Swale
Richmond
DL10 7SN
North Yorkshire
F: **01748 810228**
E: **r.townsend@yorkshiregame.co.uk**
W: **www.yorkshiregame.co.uk**

Pies

Vale of Mowbray Ltd

Vale of Mowbray has been producing pork pies in Leeming Bar since 1928. Since then the recipe has been perfected, giving a crispy baked pastry, filled with succulent cured meat, producing the "flavour to savour". We have national pork pie distribution and regional van sales with a larger product catalogue.

Details

Paul Keeton
01677 422661
20 Leases Road
Leeming Bar
DL7 9AW
North Yorkshire
F: **01677 424986**
W: **www.valeofmowbray.co.uk**

Pies

Voakes Pies

Voakes Pies produce award winning pork pies. These are made at our purpose built factory at Whixley Grange Farm, using pork from our own herd of pigs and the best quality ingredients. We take great care in producing a delicious pork pie for all food lovers who appreciate a quality product.

Details

Andrew or James Voakes
01423 339988
Whixley Grange
Whixley
York
YO26 8AY
North Yorkshire
F: **01423 339988**
W: **www.voakespies.co.uk**

Pies

Yorkshire Baker

A small wholesale bakery making and supplying high quality savoury products to local delis and farm shops. Range includes the famous Yorkish Pasty and speciality flavoured sausage rolls in our own all-butter puff pastry.

Details

Gill Ridgard
01653 699855
Unit 1, Westfield Road
North Grove Ind Estate, Malton
YO17 9HQ North Yorkshire
E: **gill@sisterscuisine.co.uk**
W: **www.sisterscuisine.co.uk**

Prepared food

J B Heath & Co

We produce "yellow harvest" cold-pressed rapeseed oil. Available in 250ml and 500ml bottles. Also 5ltr containers. We can also do infused oils.

Details

Louise Aconley
01944 710522
Binnington Wold Farm
Staxton, Scarborough
YO12 4TE North Yorkshire
E: **sales@yellowharvest.co.uk**
W: **www.yellowharvest.co.uk**

The Yorkshire Provender

We deviate from the norm with our recipes – daring to go where no soup manufacturer has gone before. And the combinations really work. We use as much fresh, regional produce as possible and work with seasonal ranges to achieve this. The product is, therefore, essentially about provenance, quality, innovation and vibrancy.

Details

Terry Williams
01765 641920
Unit 5E Keld Close
Barker Business Park
Melmerby, Ripon
HG4 5NB
North Yorkshire
F: **01765 641213**
E: **info@theyorkshireprovender.co.uk**
W: **www.theyorkshireprovender.co.uk**

Breckenholme Trading Company

All of our rapeseed oil is pressed on our farm in Thixendale, supporting low food miles using only locally sourced rapeseed. High in Omega 3,6 and 9, and naturally low in saturated fat, rapeseed oil makes a healthy and tasty alternative to other cooking oils.

Details

Adam Palmer
01759 368337
North Breckenholme Farm
Thixendale, Malton
YO17 9LS North Yorkshire
E: **adam@btcyorkshire.com**
W: **www.btcyorkshire.com**

Did you know?

Wensleydale cheese was first made by French Cistercian monks who settled at Fors in 1150. Real Yorkshire Wensleydale is still made today at the Wensleydale Creamery in Hawes

Just Williams

Our ranges of award winning products are all handmade in traditional open pans. Most of the fruit we use is handpicked from local gardens, orchards and wild hedgerows. From bullace jelly to hedgerow butter, quince cheese to wild bramble jam, we specialise in the unusual. Treat yourself.

Details

William Ramsbottom
07775 670134
9 High Street
Gilling West
Richmond
DL10 5JB
North Yorkshire
E: **william@just-williams.com**
W: **www.just-williams.com**

Raydale Preserves

Raydale Preserves is a family run business established by husband and wife team, Derek and Lesley Kettlewell. We pride ourselves on using traditional methods to produce our products. All of our products are made traditionally in small pans, ensuring our preserves are of the highest quality.

Details

Derek Kettlewell
01969 650233
School House Farm
Stalling Busk
Leyburn
DL8 3DH
North Yorkshire
F: **01969 650233**
W: **www.raydalepreserves.co.uk**

Preserves, honey, condiments & spices

Rosebud Preserves

Manufacturer of a range of over fifty products – jams, jellies, marmalades, chutneys, mustard and relishes – since 1989. Our preserves are made by hand, in small batches, using traditional methods and are characterised by bold natural flavours and natural sets, achieved without the addition of colourings, preservatives or additives, using the best available ingredients bought and gathered locally whenever possible.

Details

Elspeth Biltoft
01765 689174
Rosebud Farm
Healey, Masham, Ripon
HG4 4LH North Yorkshire
F: **01765 689174**
E: **elspeth@rosebud.fsworld.co.uk**
W: **www.rosebudpreserves.co.uk**

Preserves, honey, condiments & spices

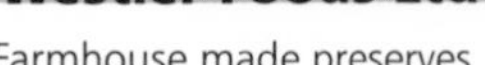

Westler Foods Ltd

Farmhouse made preserves and chutneys sold via speciality shows and the internet. White Rose Preserves Company produces natural marmalades chutneys dessert toppings and preserves on our family farm in Leyburn, Wensleydale.

Details

Robert Burns
01653 693971
Amotherby, Malton YO17 6TQ
North Yorkshire
F: **01653 600187**
E: **robert.burns@westler.com**

White Rose Preserves

Farmhouse made preserves and chutneys sold via speciality shows and the internet. White Rose Preserves produces natural marmalades, chutneys, dessert toppings and preserves on our family farm in Leyburn.

Details

Helen Sunter
01969 624806
Hill Top Farm, Moor Road
Leyburn DL8 5DJ
North Yorkshire
F: **01969 623 565**
E: **info@whiterosepreserves.co.uk**

Café & tearoom

Bettys Café Tea Rooms

Bettys is a traditional family business. For many, a visit to Yorkshire isn't complete without a trip to one of the six Bettys Café Tea Rooms. You can find us in Harrogate, Ilkley, Northallerton and York.

Details
01423 814000
Bettys & Taylors of Harrogate
1 Parliament Street
Harrogate
HG1 2QU
W: **www.bettysandtaylors.co.uk**

Café & tearoom

The Corner Café Ltd

If it's a morning coffee, snack or light lunch in the Cafe-Bar; or a full blown evening meal in our fully licensed restaurant, you will find we have something to offer everyone.

Details
Rachael Carline
01723 512261
16 Bellvue Crescent
Filey YO14 9AD
North Yorkshire
E: **thecornercafeltd@googlemail.com**

Café Harlequin

Café Harlequin uses only the freshest, regionally sourced products, offering one of the best afternoon teas in whole of Yorkshire. Our finest coffee is also available to retail and wholesale.

Details
Marie Howell
01904 630631
2 Kings Square, York YO1 8BH
North Yorkshire
E: **marie@cafeharlequin.talktalkbusinesshosting.co.uk**
W: **www.cafeharlequin.com**

Kings Square Café

Relaxed café with a warm atmosphere, overlooking Kings Square. Serving traditional breakfasts along with a variety of dishes not found elsewhere with a strong emphasis on home cooking and local sourcing.

Details
Angela Hawes
01904 631662
28 Colliergate
York
YO1 8BN
North Yorkshire

Café & tearoom

Fountains Abbey & Studley Royal

THE NATIONAL TRUST

At Fountains Abbey & Studley Royal we offer a selection of hot and cold food that is healthy, delicious and sourced and prepared to the highest standards in our restaurant and tearoom. We encourage the use of seasonal produce, favour high quality local suppliers and use organic produce wherever possible.

Details
Andrew Aikman
01765 608888
Estate Office
Fountains Abbey
Ripon
HG4 3DY
North Yorkshire
F: **01765 601002**
E: **fountainsenquiries@nationaltrust.org.uk**
W: **www.fountainsabbey.org.uk**

Café & tearoom

The Glass House Cafe Bistro

An elegant modern cafe transforming into a bistro on Thursday, Friday and Saturday evenings from 6.30pm. Situated in beautiful parkland, we serve Italian coffees, fine teas and light snacks during the day, inside or outside. We cater for food allergies and intolerances and aim to make your visit a memorable experience.

Details

Lesley Humphries
01723 368791
Northstead Manor Gardens
Burniston Road
Scarborough
YO12 6PF
North Yorkshire
E: **info@glasshousebistro.co.uk**
W: **www.glasshousebistro.co.uk**

Café & tearoom

Just-Delicious

Just-Delicious takes a real pride in producing their great taste, award winning home baked products. We offer a mouth-watering display of stunning cakes, scones and savouries. Why not pop in and have a light bite to eat or take home some real treats today. See you soon!

Details

Donna Clark
01423 711595
Kings Court
Pateley Bridge
Harrogate
HG3 5JW
North Yorkshire
E: **de_clark2004@yahoo.co.uk**
W: **www.just-delicious.co.uk**

Café & tearoom

The Lavender House

A farm shop and tearooms between the villages of Crayke and Brandsby. Premium quality local foods served in a beautiful sunny courtyard. Browse the shop and gardens, and visit the small animals and pigs.

Details

Alison Murray
01347 889369
Mill Green Farm, Crayke, York
YO61 4TT North Yorkshire
F: **01347 889368**
E: **info@lavenderhousefarmshop.co.uk**
W: **www.lavenderhousefarmshop.co.uk**

The Pig & Pastry

Delicatessen and coffee shop offering outside catering and selling Yorkshire produce and homebaked breads using organic local flours.

Details

Steven Holding
01904 675115
35 Bishopthorpe Rd
York YO23 1NA
North Yorkshire
E: **thepigandpastry@hotmail.com**

é & tearoom

eahee! spresso Bar

estled in Easingwolds harming Georgian square, eaHee! is a warm and jovial afe serving fabulous local roduce to a multi-award vinning standard. Soups, alads and panini are the basis f a menu peppered with an clectic mix of seasonal specials nd homemade, indulgent weet treats.

Details

Sophie Smith
01347 823533
Tollbooth Cottage
Market Place
Easingwold York
YO61 3AB
North Yorkshire
E: **mail@teahee.co.uk**
W: **www.teahee.co.uk**

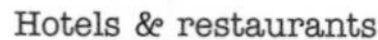

Hotels & restaurants

17 Burgate

Five star gold, award winning townhouse B&B between the marketplace and the castle in one of Yorkshire's most attractive market towns. Best local produce used in breakfasts and afternoon teas.

Details

Pat Oxley
01751 473463
17 Burgate
Pickering
YO18 7AU
North Yorkshire
E: **info@17burgate.co.uk**
W: **www.17burgate.co.uk**

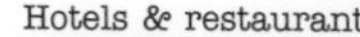

Hotels & restaurants

The Abbey Inn

19th century inn with stunning views of Byland Abbey, serving Yorkshire food with a modern spin. With one AA Rosette, the menu changes seasonally using fresh local produce including organic flour for homemade bread rolls, organic meat and our own delicious Byland Blue cheese. Local real ales and an extensive wine list. Three en-suite bedrooms – AA 5-star.

Details

Paul Tatham
01347 868204
Byland Abbey
Coxwold
YO61 4BD
North Yorkshire
E: **abbeyinn@english-heritage.org.uk**
W: **www.bylandabbeyinn.com**

Hotels & restaurants

Alexandra House

Come and enjoy a deliciouslyorkshire breakfast at Alexandra House in our sunny dining room. All our ingredients are locally sourced from the Yorkshire region.

Details
Carol Brown
01723 503205
21 West Street, Scarborough
YO11 2QR North Yorkshire
E: **info@scarborough-alexandra.co.uk**
W: **www.scarborough-alexandra.co.uk**

Hotels & restaurants

All Seasons Guest House

We pride ourselves on quality produce, sourced locally, to give you the best possible start to your day. Choose from Masham speciality sausages and Doreen's award winning Black Pudding.deliciouslyorkshire Breakfast Members.

Details
Lesley Burr
01723 515321
11 Rutland Street
Filey
YO14 9JA
North Yorkshire
E: **lesley@allseasonsfiley.co.uk**
W: **www.allseasonsfiley.co.uk**

Alvera Court

Small and privately owned, offering twelve individually decorated bedrooms. VisitBritain 4-star guest accommodation. Located opposite the International Conference Centre, with a short stroll to the town centre and the bus/train stations.

Details
Colin Grant
01423 505735
76 Kings Road, Harrogate
HG1 5JX North Yorkshire
E: **reception@alvera.co.uk**
W: **www.alvera.co.uk**

Did you know?

100,123

There are 100,123 dairy cows in the county – a twelfth of the English total.

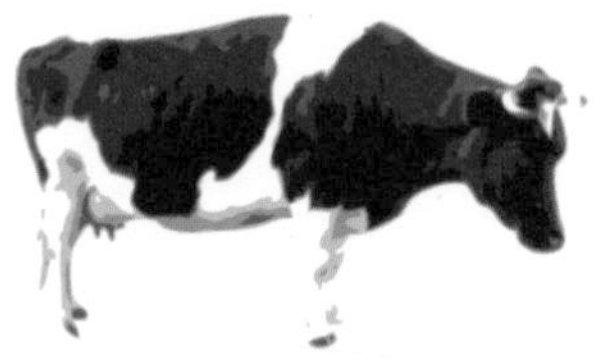

Hotels & restaurants

The Anvil Inn

We are a small but beautiful country dining pub serving homemade, fine dining meals. We welcome drinkers and diners alike to our 300 year-old, converted forge. We use fresh produce from within the county and ensure that any other wholesaler is as close as possible – food miles and beer miles count!

Details
Mark Wilson
01723 859896
Main Street
Sawdon
Scarborough
YO13 9DY
North Yorkshire
E: **info@theanvilinnsawdon.co.uk**
W: **www.theanvilinnsawdon.co.uk**

tels & restaurants

Arnot House

ᴧrnot House is a late Victorian ɨown House with three en-suite ɉuest rooms. Terms include a ɹull English buffet breakfast ɨsing many local products as ʋell as homemade breads, ɩreserves and baked products.

Details
Kim & Ann Robbins
01904 641966
7 Grosvenor Terrace
ork
O30 7AG
lorth Yorkshire
W: **www.arnothouseyork.co.uk**

Hotels & restaurants

Ashbourne House

Eight tastefully furnished bedrooms combine convenience with comfortable living perfectly. Expect the tastiest breakfast to start your day with food locally sourced from free range farms.

Details
Paul Adams
01904 639912
139 Fulford Road
York YO10 4HG
North Yorkshire
F: **01904 631332**
W: **www.ashbournehouseyork.co.uk**

Hotels & restaurants

Atlanta Hotel

Long established, B&B in Scarborough, 4-star ETC rated. Superb, spacious en-suite rooms and excellent home cooked food – with evening dinner always available. Walker and cyclist friendly – with secure parking for bikes.

Details
Eddie Blakeley
01723 360996
60-62 Columbus Ravine
Scarborough YO12 7QU
North Yorkshire
E: **info@atlanta-hotel.co.uk**
W: **www.atlanta-hotel.co.uk**

Ascot Lodge Guest House

Receive a warm welcome at this beautiful mid-Victorian guesthouse on the west side of York. Peaceful, luxurious, en-suite double, family and single rooms. Secure, private car park. Vegetarians catered for.

Details
Sandra Hudson
01904 798234
112 Acomb Road
York YO24 4EY
North Yorkshire
F: **01904 786742**
E: **info@ascotlodge.com**
W: **www.ascotlodge.com**

Ashfield B&B

Welcome to a peaceful haven close to Pickering town centre. Come and sample for yourself some of the best hospitality North Yorkshire has to offer, or do get in touch to find out more.

Details
Debbie Woodward
01751 477429
Ruffa Lane
Pickering
YO18 7HN
North Yorkshire
E: **info@ashfield-house.co.uk**
W: **www.ashfield-house.co.uk**

Did you know?

Yorkshire Pudding was first referred to in a cookery book in 1747 – The Art of Cookery Made Plain and Easy by Hannah Glasse. "It is an exceeding good pudding, the gravy of the meat eats well with it," she said

Hotels & restaurants

Ashberry Hotel

The Ashberry is located in York. Charming Victorian house situated on The Mount, gateway to the city. Five minutes walk to city walls, ten minutes to city centre, railway station, racecourse, Minster and all other tourist attractions.

Details

Kevin Lyon
01904 647339
103 The Mount
York
YO24 1AX
North Yorkshire
F: **01904 733698**
E: **kevlyon@ashberryhotel.co.uk**
W: **www.ashberryhotel.com**

Hotels & restaurants

The Austwick Traddock

TRADDOCK

Open minded as to what makes a fine meal, The Austwick Traddock's award winning restaurant uses local and seasonal ingredients, organic whenever possible. Our rooms are individually designed with most enjoying impressive views of the surrounding Dales. There is also ample parking in the grounds of the hotel.

Details

Jane & Bruce Reynolds
01524 251224
Austwick
Lancaster
LA2 8BY
North Yorkshire
E: **jane@thetraddock.co.uk**

Bank Villa Guest House

Comfortable accommodation, award winning breakfast and dinner. Book a table in our licensed restaurant or visit our seasonal cafe. Both offering home cooked local and home grown produce.

Details

Elizabeth Howard-Barker
01765 689605
Masham
Ripon HG4 4DB
North Yorkshire
W: **www.bankvilla.com**

Barker Stakes Farm

Four star, 18th century, eight-bedroom farmhouse bed and breakfast with self catering accommodation. All rooms ground floor, situated around a courtyard.

Details

Steven Goodfellow
01751 476759
Lendales Lane, Pickering
YO18 8EE North Yorkshire
E: **steve@barkerstakesfarm.com**
W: **www.barkerstakesfarm.com**

Bay Tree House

Baytree House, Harrogate is ideally located right in the heart of North Yorkshire, perfect for those looking for a short stay. We're here to make your stay enjoyable and memorable.

Details
Simon & Amanda Picton
01423 564493
98 Franklin Road, Harrogate, North Yorkshire HG1 5EN
F: **01423 563 554**
E: **info@baytreeharrogate.co.uk**
W: **www.baytreeharrogate.co.uk**

Best Western Ox Pasture Hall

Ox Pasture Hall is stunningly located in 17 acres of its own landscaped gardens and grounds, nestled amongst the meadows and woodlands of the magnificent North Yorkshire Moors National Park.

Details
Nicolas Nasser
01723 365295
Lady Edith Drive
Throxenby
Scarborough YO12 5TD
North Yorkshire
E: **slconway@aol.com**

Hotels & restaurants

Bentley Hotel

The Bentley is an elegant Victorian town house situated just 10 minutes walk from the historic centre of York. All our rooms are en-suite and prettily decorated with fresh, colourful linen, interesting pictures, a hospitality tray and even a mini decanter of sherry. A superb breakfast, which includes home-baked bread and homemade marmalade and jam, is one of the highlights of a stay at the Bentley.

Details
M Bradley
01904 644313
25 Grosvenor Terrace
York
YO3 7AG
North Yorkshire
E: **enquiries@bentleyofyork.com**
W: **www.bentleyofyork.com**

Hotels & restaurants

Black Swan Hotel

Nestling on the edge of the North Yorkshire Moors National Park, The Black Swan Hotel in Helmsley, Yorkshire is within easy reach of Whitby, York and Harrogate. Guests come here for a variety of reasons – romantic interludes, great food, our Verbena Spa, boutique shopping, walking, weddings and even business meetings... not forgetting our award-winning Tearoom & Patisserie.

Details
Chris Falcus
01439 770466
Market Place
Helmsley
YO62 5BJ
North Yorkshire
E: **chrisf@blackswan-helmsley.co.uk**
W: **www.blackswan-helmsley.co.uk**

Hotels & restaurants

The Black Swan Oldstead

The Black Swan at Oldstead is a 16th century inn, full of atmosphere and charm. The two AA rosette restaurant offers a carefully balanced choice of exiting innovative dishes and refined classical favourites strongly tied to the seasonal availability of top quality ingredients from local producers.

Details

Anne Banks
01347 868387
The Black Swan
Olstead, York
YO61 4BL
North Yorkshire
E: **anne@blackswanoldstead.co.uk**
W: **www.blackswanoldstead.co.uk**

Hotels & restaurants

Bleikers at the Malt Shovel

Country Inn, 10 minutes north of Harrogate. The Bleikers have a wealth of experience in food, hospitality and the world of opera. The family are committed to great food using the finest local ingredients, fine wine, beautifully-kept cask ales, impeccable service and the warmest of welcomes.

Details

Jane Bleiker
01423 862929
Main Street, Brearton
Harrogate
HG3 3BX
North Yorkshire
E: **bleikers@themaltshovelbrearton.co.uk**
W: **www.themaltshovelbrearton.co.uk**

Hotels & restaurants

The Boars Head Hotel

The Boars Head is a 25 bedroom luxury country house hotel, with a 2 Rosette fine dining room and a busy bar bistro.

Details

Steve Chesnutt
01423 771888
Ripley Near Harrogate
HG3 3AY North Yorkshire
E: **reservations@boarsheadripley.co.uk**
W: **www.ripleycastle.co.uk**

Bowmans Guest House

A warm Yorkshire welcome awaits you at Bowmans! Bowmans is a traditional three-storey Victorian terrace house situated just five minutes walk from York City Centre and York Minster.

Details

Debra Bowman
01904 622204
33 Grosvenor Terrace
York YO30 7AG
North Yorkshire
E: **info@bowmansguesthouse.co.uk**
W: **www.bowmansguest.co.uk**

Bootham Gardens Guesthouse

Purpose built 4-star hotel-type guesthouse where we combine our passions for people, cooking and gardening. We are a city centre breakfast restaurant for guests with private off road parking. Whilst we use local produce – many of our suppliers have won national or regional recognition.

Details

Ian Barnard
01904 625911
47 Bootham Crescent
York
YO30 7AJ
North Yorkshire
E: **guesthouse@hotmail.co.uk**
W: **www.bootham-gardens-guesthouse.co.uk**

Hotels & restaurants

Broom House

Offering 4-star silver accommodation in the picturesque village of Egton Bridge, this tranquil guest house sits on a hill with wonderful countryside views from every room.

Details
David White
01947 895279
Broom House Lane
Egton Bridge
Whitby YO21 1XD
North Yorkshire
E: **mw@broom-house.co.uk**

Cedar Court Hotel Harrogate

Cedar Court prides itself on sourcing local produce and food in our menus. Our current group initiative has been our successful Yorkshire Breakfast menu in all of our hotels.

Details
Michael Weaver
01423 858585
Park Parade
Harrogate
HG1 5AH
North Yorkshire
E: **info@cedarcourthotels.co.uk**
W: **www.cedarcourthotels.co.uk**

Hotels & restaurants

The Cayley Arms, Brompton-by-Sawdon

At the Cayley Arms a warm welcome and delicious home cooked fayre using the best seasonal ingredients from the local area await you. Our extensive range of wines and cask ales complement our dining experience, which can be enjoyed either in the pub or on our attractive terrace and garden.

Details

Jo Massingham &
Laura Hutton
01723 859372
High Street
Brompton-By-Sawdon
Scarborough
YO13 9DA
North Yorkshire

Hotels & restaurants

The Carlton Lodge (The Stirrings Ltd)

Situated on the edge of the North Yorkshire Moors National Park, the silver award winning Carlton Lodge operates under a Sustainable Visitor Charter awarded by the National Park.

Details

Chris Parkin
01439 770557
Bondgate, Helmsley, York
YO62 5EY North Yorkshire
E: **chris@carlton-lodge.com**
E: **info@carlton-lodge.com**
W: **www.carlton-lodge.com**

The Clarence Gardens

The Clarence Gardens Hotel has some of the most spectacular seaviews in Scarborough. Our rooms are great value and priced from just £39.95 per night.

Details

Helen Dean
01723 374884
4-5 Blenheim Terrace
Scarborough YO12 7HF
North Yorkshire
F: **01723 372174**
E: **helen@scarboroughlodge.force9.co.uk**

Hotels & restaurants

Cedarbarn Farm Shop & Cafe

Cedarbarn Farm Shop and butchery specialising in our own pure bred Aberdeen Angus beef, lamb, local outdoor reared pork, homemade sausages and beefburgers, home grown and local vegetables, homemade cakes, pies and ready meals. Award winning café in a beautiful setting, surrounded by P.Y.O. soft fruit fields.

Details

Karl Avison
01751 475614
Thornton Road
Pickering
YO18 7JX
North Yorkshire
E: **cedarbarn@btconnect.com**

Hotels & restaurants

Chequers Inn

The recently developed Chequers Inn has maintained its traditional roots, and boasts a fantastic beer garden overlooking the countryside. The extensive menu is prepared by an award winning kitchen team, and is well complemented by an extensive range of wines and cask ales. There are also luxury letting rooms to allow for an extended stay.

Details

Alex Main
01423 359637
Church Lane
Bilton-in-Ainsty
YO26 7NN
North Yorkshire
W: **www.thechequersbilton.co.uk**

Clocktower at Rudding Park

f food is your passion, then ook no further than Clocktower, vith daily menus using local, easonal ingredients. Dine in he restaurant underneath the triking pink glass chandelier rom Nice, relax in the bright conservatory alongside the 400 year-old olive tree or imply enjoy a drink at the cosmopolitan bar.

Details

Rebecca Hill
01423 871350
Rudding Park
Follifoot
Harrogate
HG3 1JH
North Yorkshire
W: **www.ruddingpark.co.uk**

The Coniston Hotel

Centered round a 24-acre lake, the 50 bedroom Coniston Hotel is the ideal destination for leisure breaks, fine dining, weddings, conferencing and corporate activities.

Details

Louise Bolton
01756 748080
Coniston Cold
Skipton
BD23 4EA
North Yorkshire
E: **sales@theconistonhotel.com**

Crakehall Watermill B & B

Bed & Breakfast and self-catering holiday cottage accommodation in the pretty village of Crakehall, in North Yorkshire near Bedale and the Yorkshire Dales.

Details

Lionel Barnes
01677 423240
Little Crakehall
Bedale DL8 1HU
North Yorkshire
E: **stay@crakehallwatermill.co.uk**
W: **www.crakehallwatermill.co.uk**

The Croft

Whether it's a base from which to explore Scarborough and North Yorkshire's many and varied attractions or just somewhere to relax in comfortable surroundings, The Croft is child friendly and offers good food and hospitality.

Details

Gerald Wilcock
01723 373904
87 North Marine Road
Scarborough
YO12 7HT
North Yorkshire
E: **information@crofthotel co.uk**
W: **www.crofthotel.co.uk**

The Crown Hotel

Offering a warm Yorkshire welcome, hand pulled Black Sheep ale, beef aged on the bone and The Crown grill menu featuring locally sourced produce.

Details

Richard Cox
01423 322328
Horsefair
Boroughbridge
YO51 9LB
North Yorkshire

Hotels & restaurants

The Crown & Cushion

Our attractive beamed public house with roaring log fires, is a great place to relax and enjoy a bar snack or meal from our a la carte menu. We are particularly well known for our game dishes and, wherever possible, we source all ingredients locally or from the nearby coast.

Details

Christopher Bennett & Claire Garbutt
01653 618304
Main Street
Welburn
YO60 7DZ
North Yorkshire
W: **www.crownandcushionwelburn.co.uk**

Hotels & restaurants

The Crown Inn Roecliffe

A lovely refurbished 16th century coaching Inn. Stone flag floors, crackling open fires, a wealth of solid oak beams and a medieval barn function room. The food emphasis is on locally sourced, fresh, classic pub dishes – anything from a steak & ale pie to a dozen fresh oysters.

Details

Karl Mainey
01423 322300
Roecliffe
Boroughbridge
YO51 9LY
North Yorkshire
F: **01423 322033**
E: **karl.mainey@btconnect.com**
W: **www.crowninnroecliffe.com**

Hotels & restaurants

Crown Spa Hotel

Dine in 4-star hotel venue Taste Restaurant where European fuses with traditional Yorkshire cuisine, created with locally sourced ingredients. Our Spa Pamper Treatments and Taste Restaurant welcome non-residents.

Details

David Frank
01723 357400
Esplanade
Scarborough
YO11 2AG
North Yorkshire
E: **davidfrank@crownspahotel.com**
W: **www.crownspahotel.co.uk**

otels & restaurants

Derwent House Guest House

The welcoming Derwent House Hotel is a fully licensed non smoking family run hotel, open all year round for holiday-makers, business travellers and those looking for a short break.

Details
Keith Pratt
01723 373880
6 Rutland Terrace, Queens Parade
Scarborough YO12 7JB
North Yorkshire
E: **info@derwenthousehotel.co.uk**
W: **www.derwenthousehotel.co.uk**

Hotels & restaurants

The Devonshire Fell Hotel & Restaurant

Our guests never cease to be entranced by the stunning views. A combination of delicious local food, great wine and supremely comfortable bedrooms.

Details
01756 729000
Burnsall
Nr Skipton
BD23 6BT
North Yorkshire
W: **www.devonshirefell.co.uk**

Hotels & restaurants

The Ellenby

A family run B&B, with panoramic sea views overlooking the magnificent North Bay. Awarded 4-star for comfort and quality – retaining the individual personal touch.

Details
John & Eliza Fail
01723 372916
95-97 Queen Parade
Scarborough
YO12 7HY
North Yorkshire
E: **johngail@aol.com**
W: **www.theellenby.co.uk**

Devonshire Arms (Bolton Abbey) Ltd

Gracious unstuffy country estate hotel with two restaurants (Michelin star fine dining and vibrant bar brasserie), private dining, bedrooms and health spa. Delicious tasty food served using the best of extensive kitchen gardens, local landscape and seascape.

Details
Andy Nicholson
01756 710441
Bolton Abbey
Skipton BD23 6AJ
North Yorkshire
E: **andy.nicholson@devonshirehotels.co.uk**

Dunsley Hall Country House Hotel

Dunsley Hall's award winning restaurant provides locally supplied ingredients and seafood is our speciality. Lunchtime, early evening meals and snacks in the Pyman Bar provide a light alternative.

Details
Bill Ward
01947 893437
Dunsley
Whitby
YO4 3TL
North Yorkshire
E: **reception@dunsleyhall.com**

Elmfield House

Country guesthouse offering a peaceful night and hearty breakfast. Most ingredients sourced within 10 miles, including free range eggs, organic dairy produce, local smoked fish, traditional sausages, bacon and preserves.

Details
Astra Towning
01677 450558
Arrathorne, Bedale DL8 1NE
North Yorkshire
E: **stay@elmfieldhouse.co.uk**
W: **www.elmfieldhouse.co.uk**

Hotels & restaurants

The Farthings

Experience that famous Yorkshire hospitality at this award winning, family run, 4-star guest house, situated near the famous city walls. Indulge in a deliciouslyyorkshire breakfast using local produce.

Details

Helen Milner

01904 653545

5 Nunthorpe Avenue
York YO23 1PF
North Yorkshire

E: **stay@farthingsyork.co.uk**

W: **www.farthingsyork.co.uk**

Did you know?

There are 84 breweries in the historic county of Yorkshire, the oldest of which is Samuel Smith's Old Brewery at Tadcaster, founded in 1758.

Hotels & restaurants

Feversham Arms Hotel and Verbena Spa

Situated in the picturesque market town of Helmsley, this 'Small Luxury Hotel of the World' has 33 luxurious rooms, 22 of which are suites. The Verbena Spa has a heat experience suite, heated outdoor pool, hot-tub and a full range of Elemis treatments. The restaurant has been awarded 2 rosettes and serves delicious, fresh seasonal food.

Details

Simon Rhatigan

01439 770766

Helmsley
York YO62 5AG
North Yorkshire

E: **info@fevershamarmshotel.com**

W: **www.fevershamarmshotel.com**

Hotels & restaurants

Flamborough Rigg Cottage

A peaceful oasis with all the warmth of a home from home combined with the style and facilities of a boutique hotel. We offer beautifully cooked dinners and breakfasts using local ingredients.

Details

Philip Jackson

01751 475263

Middle Head Road, Stape,
Pickering, North Yorkshire
YO18 8HR

E: **enquiries@flamboroughriggcottage.co.uk**

Foulskye Farm House B&B

Foulsyke farm is set on a working farm in the picturesque village of Scalby. Our family run bed and breakfast is perfect for a relaxing holiday or as a base for many outdoor activities.

Details

Jayne Pickup

01723 507423

Barmoor Lane, Scalby
Scarborough, North Yorkshire
YO13 0PG

E: **jaynepickup@btinternet.com**

W: **www.foulsykefarmhouse.co.uk**

The Four Alls Inn

Neville, Helen and Richard bid you a warm welcome at the Four Alls Inn family run pub. Located on the busy A64 the pub is the perfect eatery when out for the day in Yorkshire, visiting York or on the way to the coast. The well priced menu is full of family favourites with the meat and produce sourced locally.

Details

Neville Flowitt
01904 468233
Malton Road
York
YO32 9TW
North Yorkshire
E: **nevilleR@flowitt.orangehome.co.uk**

Gallon House

Overlooking Knaresborough's beautiful Nidd Gorge, Gallon House offers charming, award winning accommodation in a breathtaking setting. Well known Yorkshire chef Rick Hodgson takes pleasure in creating bespoke menus for guests using local seasonal produce.

Details

Rick and Sue Hodgson
01423 862102
47 Kirkgate
Knaresborough
HG5 8BZ
North Yorkshire
E: **gallon-house@ntlworld.com**
W: **www.gallon-house.co.uk**

The Gallery

Kathryn & Steve welcome you to their home, a Grade II listed building dating back to the 17th century, offering luxurious bed & breakfast accommodation without losing the charm of its many original features.

Details

Kathryn Collington
01845 523767
18 Kirkgate
Thirsk
YO7 1PQ
North Yorkshire
E: **kathryn@gallerybedandbreakfast.co.uk**
W: **www.gallerybedandbreakfast.co.uk**

George & Dragon Inn

John and Collette welcome you to our lovely country inn. Relax in our delightful 4-star rooms, indulge in our rosette award winning food and extensive wine list. Serving local ales. Surprised you will be.

Details

C Wormwell
01969 663358
Aysgarth, Leyburn DL8 3AD
North Yorkshire
F: **01969 663773**
E: **ganddinn@hotmail.com**
W: **www.georgeanddragonaysgarth.co.uk**

Hotels & restaurants

The General Tarleton Inn

Bar/brasserie, restaurant and rooms, serving food with Yorkshire roots. AA 5-star accommodation, 2 rosettes for food, Michelin Bib Gourmand. We take great care in sourcing the best local produce available from farmers and producers who care as passionately as we do about food.

Details

John Topham
01423 340284
Boroughbridge Road
Ferrensby, Knaresborough
HG5 0PZ North Yorkshire
E: **gti@generaltarleton.co.uk**
W: **www.generaltarleton.co.uk**

Hotels & restaurants

Gisborough Hall Hotel

Set in peaceful private grounds on the edge of the North York Moors. Whether your interest in our beautiful hotel is for business or for pleasure, you will be guaranteed a very warm welcome.

Details

Julie Diggles
0844 8799149
Whitby Lane
Guisborough
TS14 6PT
North Yorkshire
E: **julie.diggles@macdonald-hotels.co.uk**

The Golden Fleece Hotel

Lovely old coaching inn serving wonderful Yorkshire breakfast and traditional food. Excellent Sunday lunch, great value at £12.95 p p. 23 bedrooms all ensuite, a great venue for touring the moors and dales.

Details

Jo Grewcock
01845 523108
Market Place
Thirsk YO7 1LL
North Yorkshire
E: **reservations@goldenfleecehotel.com**

Hotels & restaurants

The Green Room Restaurant

The Green Room Restaurant in Victoria Road, Scarborough is the perfect place to eat. Seasonal, local foods used in imaginative early evening and a la carte menus, great wine list, fantastic service. To reserve your table, telephone 01723 501801. More information: www.thegreenroomrestaurant.com.
Michelin recommended.

Details

Robert Porter
01723 501801
138 Victoria Road
Scarborough
YO11 1SL
North Yorkshire
W: **www.thegreenroomrestaurant.com**

tels & restaurants

;reens Seafood ₹estaurant

;reens prides themselves on ourcing and using the finest ıf local produce, whether it be resh turbot from Whitby quay ır Yorkshire lamb from Ryedale. Ve are committed to serving 'ou the best quality of 'orkshire produce available.

)etails
₹ob Green
)1947 600284
3 Bridge Street
Vhitby
'O22 4BG
Iorth Yorkshire
V: **www.greensofwhitby.com**

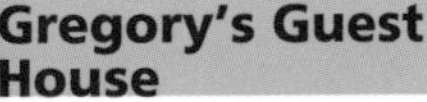

Hotels & restaurants

Grimston House

Four star, friendly guest house in two acres of lovely gardens. Village location five miles from York on the bus route. Serves a delicious Yorkshire breakfast. Two minutes from local pub, which serves wonderful home cooked food.

Details
Pat Wright
01904 728328
Deighton
York
YO19 6HB
North Yorkshire
E: **pat_wright@btinternet.com**

Gregory's Guest House

Our deliciouslyorkshire breakfast, using locally sourced ingredients, has become a real favourite for our guests here at Gregory's Guest House in York. Please see our website: gregorys.york@virgin.net

Details
Beverley and Martin Gregory
01904 627521
160 Bishopthorpe Road
York YO23 1LF
North Yorkshire
E: **gregorys.york@virgin.net**
W: **www.gregorysofyork.co.uk**

The Hawthornes Bed and Breakfast

With complementary tea and homemade scones on arrival, we pride ourselves on making you feeling at home and relaxed. Providing spacious and comfortable en-suite rooms to make your stay as relaxing as possible.

Details
Paula Appleby
01751 474755
High Back Side, Middleton,
Pickering YO18 8PB
North Yorkshire
E: **paulaappleby@btinternet.com**
W: **www.the-hawthornes.co.uk**

Did you know?

World-renowned British retailer Marks and Spencer started as a stall at Kirkgate Market, Leeds in 1884. The first stall is marked today with a green and gold commemorative clock.

Hotels & restaurants

High Catton Grange

Delightful 18th century farmhouse B&B using locally sourced produce. This relaxing oasis awaits you after exploring Yorkshire's varied places of interest. Also self-catering cottages. Welcome to Yorkshire.

Details

Sheila Foster
01759 371374
Stamford Bridge
York YO41 1EP
North Yorkshire
E: **enquire@highcattongrange.co.uk**
W: **www.highcattongrange.co.uk**

Hotels & restaurants

The Highwayman

Gavin and Lucy bid you a warm welcome and ask you to indulge in their fine menu composed entirely from locally sourced supplies. Alternatively take a Yorkshire pint from the cask ale range and relax in their beautiful Beer Garden. While in the village don't forget to stay a while and take in a walk or learn the history of Sheriff Hutton.

Details

Gavin & Lucy Greenbank
01347 878328
The Square
Sheriff Hutton
York
YO60 6QZ
North Yorkshire
E: **highwaymanyork@aol.com**
W: **www.thehighwaymanyork.co.uk**

Hotels & restaurants

Herriots Hotel

Tastefully decorated accommodation brimming with comfort and character. Delicious food, large selection of beers, quality cask ales and wines available to help you relax and unwind in our friendly bar or sumptuous conservatory.

Details

Susan Wilkinson
01756 792781
Broughton Road
Skipton
BD23 1RT
North Yorkshire
E: **info@herriotsforleisure.co.uk**

Did you know?

There are **1,139,348** lambs in Yorkshire (over a seventh of the English total)

Hotel Du Vin & Bistro York

Hotel du Vin York is a unique luxury boutique hotel set in a beautiful Grade II listed building. The hotel has 44 individually designed rooms and houses our trademark bistro. Here you will find simple classics that change seasonally, all supporting our philosophy of using the finest and freshest local produce, cooked simply, priced sensibly.

Details

Ammie Stowell
01904 557350
89 The Mount
York
YO24 1AX
North Yorkshire
W: **www.hotelduvin.com**

Hotels & restaurants

Inglenook Guest House

On the banks of the River Greta nestling at the foot of Ingleborough, Inglenook, with its fresh, clean rooms and friendly atmosphere, is the perfect place to relax and unwind on your well earned break.

Details

Carolyn Smith
01524 241270
20 Main Street
Ingleton
LA6 3HJ
North Yorkshire
E: **inglenook20@hotmail.com**
W: **www.inglenookguesthouse.com**

The Inn at Hawnby

This delightful country inn is perched at the top of the hill in the peaceful village of Hawnby, with stunning panoramic views of the North Yorkshire Moors. Whether it's a long lunch or lazy weekend – The Inn at Hawnby is just the perfect place.

Details

Dave & Kathryn Young
01423 546201
Hawnby, Near Helmsley
North Yorkshire
YO62 5QS
E: **info@innathawnby.co.uk**
W: **www.innathawnby.co.uk**

Hotels & restaurants

Jadellas Guest House

We serve fresh, local and organic food wherever possible, free range eggs from chickens and geese. Homemade jams and preserves. A range of teas and coffee from a local supplier.

Details

Jill Howe
01723 378811
72 Columbus Ravine
Scarborough YO12 7QU
North Yorkshire
F: **01723 378811**
E: **john@johnhowe.wanadoo.co.uk**
W: **www.jadellashotel scarborough.co.uk**

The Kensington Guest House

A friendly hotel in Scarborough offering excellent Bed and Breakfast accommodation, "Where nothing is too much trouble!"

Details

Joy White
01723 368117
66 Columbus Ravine
Scarborough
YO12 7QH
North Yorkshire
F: **01723 360601**
E: **info@kensingtonguesthouse.co.uk**

Hotels & restaurants

The Kings Head Hotel and Restaurant

A delightful family owned hotel and restaurant sited at the foot of Roseberry Topping – on the edge of the North York Moors National Park. Serving lunch and evening meals using high quality produce sourced from the local area.

Details

Michael Dickinson
01642 722318
The Green,
Newton-under-Roseberry
Great Ayton, Middlesbrough
TS9 6QR
F: **01642 724750**
E: **info@kingsheadhotel.co.uk**

Did you know?

The Bingley Arms at Bardsey, near Leeds, is the oldest pub in Britain: it's been around since AD905 and used to be called The Priests Inn as it was a popular spot for travelling monks to rest.

Hotels & restaurants

The Kimberley Hotel

The **Kimberley** Hotel

The Kimberley Hotel has recently been refurbished, providing 93 luxury bedrooms. The Terrace is a stylish new bistro at The Kimberley Hotel. The stunning menu is packed with Yorkshire produce.

Details

Mark Harrison
01423 505613
11-19 Kings Road
Harrogate
HG1 5JY
North Yorkshire
E: **info@thekimberley.co.uk**
W: **www.thekimberley.co.uk**

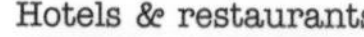

Hotels & restaurants

Lanterna

Piemontese/Italian restaurant using mainly Yorkshire ingredients specialising in local fresh fish sourced directly from Scarborough harbour at the early morning fish market. Fresh white and black truffles from Giorgio's native Piemonte, North West Italy. White Truffle Yorkshire Pudding Cookery School opening in June, featuring many seasonal dishes.

Details

Giorgio Alessio
01723 363616
33 Queen Street
Scarborough
YO11 1HQ
North Yorkshire
E: **info@giorgioalessio.co.uk**
W: **www.lanterna-ristorante.co.uk**

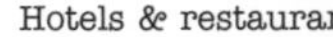

The Leeway

The Leeway is a bolt-hole in the heart of Whitby. Contemporary rooms, with memory foam mattresses, bathrobes and luxury toiletries plus excellent service to ensure a great relaxing stay.

Details

Karen Walker
01947 602604
1 Havelock Place, Whitby
YO21 3ER. North Yorkshire
E: **enquiries@theleeway.co.uk**
W: **www.theleeway.co.uk**

Linton Laith B&B

5 bedroomed luxury bed and breakfast accommodation situated in a converted barn at Grange Farm, Linton. The farm is a working farm of dairy, cattle and sheep and the conversion in 2008 of a traditional barn, provides the accommodation.

Details

Shirley Metcalfe
01756 753209
Linton-in-Craven
Skipton BD23 5HH
North Yorkshire
E: **stay@lintonlaithe.co.uk**

Hotels & restaurants

Lockwoods

Lockwoods cafébar/restaurant aims to celebrate the best of Ripon's rich Cathedral City history, whilst challenging it into the future. This theme of traditional and contemporary is reflected in our décor, our modern European menu, our wine list, and the art on our walls. We use fresh and seasonal ingredients from local producers, and look forward to welcoming you!

Details

Matthew Lockwood
01765 607555
83 North Street
Ripon
HG4 1DP
North Yorkshire
W: **www.lockwoodsrestaurant.co.uk**

Hotels & restaurants

The Lodge at Leeming Bar

A personally run hotel and restaurant which can satisfy all your eating-out, accommodation and function requirements in this area, supporting local producers and suppliers.

Details

Suzanne Bailes
01677 422122
The Great North Road
Bedale DL8 1DT
North Yorkshire
E: **thelodgeatleemingbar@btinternet.com**
W: **www.leemingbar.com**

Lovesome Hill Farm

Sample our farmhouse breakfast using our own bacon and sausages when available and homemade preserves, local organic milk and butter. Help us to collect fresh free range eggs. There are also packs of our own lamb, pork and beef available to take home.

Details

M. Pearson
01609 772311
Lovesome Hill
Northallerton
DL6 2PB
North Yorkshire

Hotels & restaurants

Low Penhowe Bed & Breakfast

A traditional Yorkshire stone-built farmhouse, with stunning views. Overlooking the Howardian Hills, Castle Howard and North Yorkshire Moors, the house makes an idyllic spot for a quiet few nights away yet close to York. 2006 & 2008 deliciouslyyorkshire Breakfast Winner.

Details
Christopher Turner
01653 658336
Burythorpe, Malton YO17 9LU
North Yorkshire
E: **lowpenhowe@btinternet.com**
W: **www.bedandbreakfastyorkshire.co.uk**

Lyndale Guesthouse

You will be made very welcome at this characteristic Victorian guest house just off the high street in this market town of Pateley Bridge. We are an ideal base for exploring the Yorkshire Dales.

Details
Lynne Gibbon
01423 712657
King Street
Pateley Bridge
HG3 5AT
North Yorkshire
E: **lyndale.guesthouse@talktalk.net**
W: **www.lyndaleguesthouse.com**

Hotels & restaurants

The Malt Shovel

Located in a picturesque village, a warm greeting awaits at the local pub. The menu is of the highest order owing to the fine local meats and produce supplied and is completed by a range of cask ales and extensive wine list. Vanessa, Julie, Jamie and Steve encourage you to dine and stay in the village a while and enjoy the charms, its rural setting or country walks.

Details
Steve Smith
01653 628264
Main Street
Hovingham
York
Y062 4LF
North Yorkshire
E: **info@themaltshovelhovingham.co.uk**
W: **www.themaltshovel hovingham.co.uk**

Hotels & restaurants

Marine View Guest House

A family-run, six bedroomed bed & breakfast in Scarborough with a friendly, relaxed and informal atmosphere. Offering comfortable bed and breakfast accommodation.

Details
Ian Rees
01723 361864
34 Blenheim Terrace
Scarborough
YO12 7HD
North Yorkshire
E: **info@marineview.co.uk**
W: **www.marineview.co.uk**

Middlethorpe Hall and Spa

Middlethorpe Hall is well known for its comfortable, luxurious atmosphere. Renowned for its imaginative cuisine and its panelled dining rooms which overlook the manicured gardens.

Details
Lionel Chatard
01904 641241
Bishopthorpe Road
York YO23 2GB
North Yorkshire
E: **info@middlethorpe.com**

Moorlands Country House

The Moorlands is a beautiful restored Victorian house set in its own grounds. We are within easy reach of York, Castle Howard, Harrogate, the dramatic North East coastline and of course, the North Yorkshire Moors.

Details

Gill Leonard
01751 460229
Levisham
Nr Pickering
YO18 7NL
North Yorkshire
E: **ronaldoleonardo@aol.com**
W: **www.moorlandslevisham.co.uk**

Hotels & restaurants

National Railway Museum

NRM
NATIONAL RAILWAY MUSEUM

First class dining. Delectable and creative cuisine is available daily in the NRM restaurant and café, against a backdrop of historic locomotives. Delicious canapés, appetising bowl food and exquisite banquets are a speciality. Freshly prepared on site and making the most of Yorkshire's finest produce, you will soon realise why we welcome visitors and guests back time and time again.

Details

Rachel Fox
01904 686219
Leeman Road
York
YO26 4XJ
North Yorkshire
W: **www.nrm-events.org.uk**

Hotels & restaurants

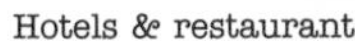

The New Inn

The New Inn is a hidden gem in the small village of Tholthorpe, the outlet recently won two accolades at the Hambleton Food Awards. Head chef and owner Cameron Reid sources all his ingredients locally and is about to embark on a Cookery School from the pub. The building is beautifully traditional: with a bar and separate restaurant, the atmosphere is set by the lighting and roaring open fires.

Details

Cameron Reid
01347 838329
Tholthorpe
York
YO61 1SL
North Yorkshire
W: **www.thenewinntholthorpe.co.uk**

Hotels & restaurants

Nethergill Farm

Large Victorian farmhouse B&B set in 400 acres of stunning moor and woodland. Luxurious bedrooms and deliciouslyorkshire breakfast with homemade bread, home cured bacon and eggs from our own very free range hens.

Details

Fiona Clark

01756 761126

Buckden, Skipton
BD23 5JS
North Yorkshire

E: **fiona.clark@nethergill.co.uk**

W: **www.nethergill.co.uk**

Oldstead Grange

Enjoy the traditional features of our 17th century farmhouse and savour our unique combination of exceptionally high quality accommodation with a relaxed friendly atmosphere.

Details

Anne Banks

01347 868634

Oldstead
Coxwold, Helmsley
YO61 4BJ
North Yorkshire

Hotels & restaurants

Peasholm Park Hotel

We are a detached hotel in Scarborough and situated in a commanding position opposite Peasholm Park, close to the North Bay of Scarborough on the East Coast of Yorkshire. We offer bed and breakfast accommodation in our comfortable guest house, close to the seafront and the new Sands Resort.

Details

Jeanette Frank

01723 500954

21-23 Victoria Park
Scarborough YO12 7TS
North Yorkshire

E: **peasholmparkhotel@btconnect.com**

W: **www.peasholmpark.co.uk**

Hotels & restaurants

Peppers Restaurant

peppers
restaurant&bar

Peppers Restaurant serves contemporary, seasonal, modern British cuisine based around the fantastic larder available to us here on the North Yorkshire coast. As well as our pre-theatre menu available 5.00pm - 7.00pm, our award winning a la carte menu is also available Tuesday to Saturday from 7.00pm until 10.00pm.

Details

J D Smith

01723 500642

First Floor
Stephen Joseph Theatre
Westborough
Scarborough
YO11 1JW
North Yorkshire

E: **peppers.restaurant@virgin.net**

W: **www.peppersrestaurant.co.uk**

otels & restaurants

Perk-up Restaurant

Award winning cafe and restaurant situated on Ripon's market square where real care is taken over the ingredients and cooking and dishes change with the local markets.

Details

Annette Lyons

01765 698888

43 Market Square

Ripon HG4 1BZ

North Yorkshire

E: **annettelyons@btinternet.com**

W: **www.perkup.co.uk**

Hotels & restaurants

The Poplars Rooms & Cottages

Ideally located for both the Dales and the Moors, offering superior accommodation with all the comforts of home, as well as a traditional Yorkshire breakfast – using only the best local produce.

Details

Amanda Richards

01845 522712

Carlton Miniott, Thirsk

YO7 4LX North Yorkshire

E: **amanda@thepoplarsthirsk.com**

W: **www.thepoplarsthirsk.com**

Hotels & restaurants

Red Lea Hotel

Superbly located on Scarborough's south cliff and close to the Esplanade Spa Cliff Lift, the Red Lea enjoys glorious sea views. Extensively refurbished with comfortable bedrooms, pleasant lounges, indoor swimming pool, great food and friendly service, the hotel offers guests a warm welcome all year round.

Details

Nick Allen

01723 362431

Prince of Wales Terrace

Scarborough

YO11 2AJ

North Yorkshire

F: **01723 374230**

E: **info@redleahotel.co.uk**

Phoenix Court

With comfortable rooms, fantastic sea views and a guest car park, Phoenix Court is perfect for your stay in Scarborough. Visit Britain 4-star rated and part of the Walkers Welcome Scheme.

Details

Alison Edwards

01723 501150

8/9 Rutland Terrace

Queens Parade, Scarborough

YO12 7JB

North Yorkshire

E: **info@hotel-phoenix.co.uk**

W: **www.hotel-phoenix.co.uk**

Rawcliffe House Farm

We have three bedrooms situated on our south facing courtyard. We are proud to have been awarded a Silver Award for Excellence from the English Tourism Council. Every morning we serve a delicious full Yorkshire Breakfast using only the finest local produce.

Details

Jan Allsopp

01751 473292

Stape

Pickering

YO18 8JA

North Yorkshire

W: **www.rawcliffehousefarm.co.uk**

Hotels & restaurants

River House Hotel

A Victorian country house, offering superb breakfasts and evening meals. Centrally located in the beautiful Malhamdale village amidst stunning scenery.

Details

Ann Roe
01729 830315
Malham
Skipton
BD23 4DA
North Yorkshire
E: **info@riverhousehotel.co.uk**

Did you know?

The Great Yorkshire Show goes back 171 years. It used to tour 30 towns before the innovative decision was made in 1950 to build a permanent showground in Harrogate.

Hotels & restaurants

The Royal Oak (Timothy Taylor)

The Royal Oak was originally built as a coaching inn and that tradition of superb hospitality certainly continues today with fantastic food, drink, stylish bedrooms and a warm welcome.

Details

Adrian Sykes
01765 602284
36 Kirkgate
Ripon
HG4 1PB
W: **www.royaloakripon.co.uk**

Hotels & restaurants

Scarborough Travel & Holiday Lodge

The Scarborough Travel and Holiday Lodge offers high quality accommodation, at affordable prices, in the heart of Scarborough. The Lodge is ideal for the business traveller and holidaymaker alike.

Details

Helen Dean
01723 363537
33 Valley Road
Scarborough
YO11 2LX
North Yorkshire
F: **01723 501239**
E: **helen.dean@hotel-group.co.uk**

Seasons

Restaurant/cafe bar serving locally sourced seasonal dishes based around a British theme with Mediterranean influences.

Details

Jane Gallogly
01748 825340
Station Buildings
Station Yard
Richmond DL10 4LD
North Yorkshire
E: **jane@restaurant-seasons.co.uk**

otels & restaurants

Smugglers Rock Country House

Georgian country house, reputedly a former smugglers' haunt between Whitby and Scarborough. Panoramic views over surrounding National Park and sea. An ideal holiday base for exploring the area, close to 'Heartbeat' country.

Details
S. Gregson
01723 870044
Staintondale Road
Ravenscar, Scarborough
YO13 0ER North Yorkshire
E: **info@smugglersrock.co.uk**
W: **www.smugglersrock.co.uk**

Hotels & restaurants

St. Aidan's Church of England High School

Leading the field in meeting stringent new regulations on school food, and bucking the national trend for declining take-up, our 20-strong catering team now serve almost 2,000 meals every school day.

Details
Marian Farrar
01423 885814
Oatlands Drive
Harrogate HG2 8JR
North Yorkshire
F: **01423 884327**
E: **m.farrar@staidans.co.uk**
W: **www.staidans.co.uk**

Hotels & restaurants

Stoney End & Stoney End Holidays

Tucked away in a quiet corner of the tiny hamlet of Worton, Stoney End Bed & Breakfast offers three bedrooms, all furnished, decorated and appointed with your comfort in mind.

Details
Pamela Hague
01969 650652
Stoney End
Worton Leyburn
DL8 3ET North Yorkshire
E: **pmh@stoneyend.co.uk**
W: **www.stoneyend.co.uk**

Southlands Guest House

Just minutes from the historic city of York and walking distance of York Races. Enjoy a locally sourced full English breakfast in our dining room before heading off to see the sights of York.

Details
Karen Greenwood
01904 675966
69 Nunmill Street York
YO23 1NT North Yorkshire
E: **southlandsguesthouse@yahoo.co.uk**
W: **www.southlands-guesthouse.co.uk**

The Star Inn

The small relaxed restaurant glows with the bonhomie of a proper old fashioned auberge – run with style! Unpretentious, good hearted genius on every plate – "adore every second of being there!"

Details
Andrew Pern
01439 770397
Harome, Nr. Helmsley
YO62 5JE
North Yorkshire
E: **jpern@thestarinnatharome.co.uk**
W: **www.thestarinnatharome.co.uk**

Did you know?

More than 90% of the world's forced rhubarb was once produced in Yorkshire - and the Yorkshire Rhubarb Triangle, between Leeds, Bradford and Wakefield, is still going strong.

Hotels & restaurants

Swinton Park

Luxury castle hotel, set in 200 acres of parkland in the Yorkshire Dales, with gardens, lakes and four acre-walled garden. Lavishly furnished with award-winning cuisine. Bird of Prey centre, spa and cookery school. Garden lunches and garden design days. Alfresco food festival with culinary trail and guided tours. Open all year, non-residents welcome.

Details

Reservations
01765 680900
Masham
Ripon
HG4 4JH
North Yorkshire
F: **01765 680901**
E: **reservations@swintonpark.com**
W: **www.swintonpark.com**

Hotels & restaurants

Tipperthwaite Barn Bed and Breakfast

A warm welcome awaits you at Tipperthwaite Barn Bed and Breakfast set on the edge of the Yorkshire Dales National Park amidst one of the largest outcrops of limestone scenery in England.

Details

Dawn Craven
01729 823146
Paley Green Lane
Giggleswick, Settle BD24 0D2
North Yorkshire
E: **stay@tipperthwaitebarn.co.uk**
W: **www.tipperthwaitebarn.co.uk**

Walgate House B&B

Graded 4-star 18th century former farmhouse set in a quiet position in the village of Burythorpe. Breakfast consists of free range eggs with locally produced bacon, sausages, black pudding and preserves.

Details

Alison Bray
01653 658101
Main Street
Burythorpe, Malton
YO17 9LJ North Yorkshire
E: **walgatehouse@aol.com**

Hotels & restaurants

The Water Rat

The Water Rat is located on the river bank of the river Skell running through Ripon and within walking distance of the centre. The beer garden and river balcony are extremely popular in the summer. The traditional surrounds of the pub are matched with a great food offer and drinks range. Children are welcome and catered for.

Details

Rick Jones
01765 602251
24 Bondgate Green
Ripon
HG4 1QW
North Yorkshire
E: **rick@thewaterrat.co.uk**
W: **www.thewaterrat.co.uk**

Hotels & restaurants

The Waverley

Located on Whitby's West Cliff we are conveniently situated for access to the town, beaches, Whitby Pavilion and other attractions. Hope to see you soon!

Details
Julie Ward
01947 604389
17 Crescent Avenue
Whitby
YO21 3ED
North Yorkshire
E: **julie@whitbywaverley.com**
W: **www.whitbywaverley.com**

Hotels & restaurants

Westfields Farm

Westfields is a lovely old farmhouse in the village of Bellerby, near Leyburn. Newly modernised, the house retains all its original charm. We have two guest rooms: four poster and super king/twin. We serve a farmer's breakfast from local suppliers and cater for all tastes.

Details
Chris Chilton
01969 622047
Moor Road
Bellerby, Leyburn
DL8 5QX North Yorkshire
E: **stay@wesfieldsfarmbandb.co.uk**

Hotels & restaurants

The Wheatsheaf Inn

Located in the centre of the village with wonderful views of the surrounding countryside. The Inn dates back to the 19th century where it was the centre of village life: and it still is today!

Details
Elaine Pulling
01947 895271
Egton, Whitby
YO21 1TZ
North Yorkshire
E: **elainepulling@hotmail.co.uk**
W: **www.wheatsheaf.com**

Well House

Georgian House set in the picturesque village of Newby Wiske. Enjoy a delicious breakfast in our conservatory overlooking our large landscaped garden. All rooms en-suite. Prices from £28.00 to £38.00 ppn.

Details
Judith Smith
01609 772253
Newby Wiske, Northallerton
DL7 9EX North Yorkshire
E: **info@wellhouse-newbywiske.co.uk**
W: **www.wellhouse-newbywiske.co.uk**

Wharncliffe Hotel

Four-star guest accommodation situated overlooking North Bay Scarborough, with glorious sea views, within a short walk of the castle, town and harbour. Ideal for couples to relax and unwind.

Details
Ann Trigg
01723 374635
26 Blenheim Terrace
Scarborough YO12 7HD
North Yorkshire
E: **info@thewharncliffescarborough.co.uk**
W: **www.thewharncliffehotel.co.uk**

The White Swan Inn

You will discover we have a clear ethos. Simple goodness from fresh ingredients that are sourced in season, properly cooked, presented and put on your table with a minimum of food miles. You will be eating at the only restaurant outside of London supplied by the famous 'Ginger Pig' farm/butchery.

Details
Lisa Fraser
01751 472288
Market Place, Pickering
YO18 7AA North Yorkshire
W: **www.white-swan.co.uk**

Hotels & restaurants

Worsley Arms Hotel

A friendly, family-run hotel that offers good quality accommodation in an exquisite country house setting with open log fires, stylish furnishings, and a warm inviting welcome. Choose to eat in the informal bar or the elegant dining room where you will find an interesting selection of freshly prepared dishes, sourced where possible from local producers.

Details

Tony Finn
01653 628234
High Street Hovingham
York
YO62 4LA
North Yorkshire
E: **worsleyarms@aol.com**
W: **www.worsleyarms.co.uk**

Hotels & restaurants

Wynnstay House

A double fronted Victorian villa offering a home from home, with all rooms ensuite. Our locally sourced Yorkshire breakfast menu includes Grimsby kippers and fabulous sausages from the Whole Hogg Sausage Co!

Details

Tracey & Andy Davis
01423 560476
60 Franklin Road
Harrogate
HG1 5EE
North Yorkshire
W: **www.wynnstayhouse.com**

Did you know?

The food and drink sector's annual contribution to the regional economy is worth £8 billion *(ONS 2008)*

Deli & independent grocers

De'Clare

We specialise in selling the very best local produce. Shepherds Purse cheeses, MacKenzies smoked fish, Angel chocolates and Glenroyd organic chutneys are just a few of the many specialist foods on sale in our deli opposite the museum gardens. Great sandwiches, cakes and coffee to take out or eat in.

Details

Clare Prowse
01904 644410
5 Lendal, York YO1 8AQ
North Yorkshire
E: **clare@declaredeli.co.uk**

Hemingbrough Store

A local store with a little bit more. Retailers of Yorkshire Dales fresh meats and poultry, speciality sausages and cooked meats, including dry cured bacon. Local award winning pies and sausage rolls, free range eggs, potatoes, fruit and veg, cakes and pastries.

Details

G A & T Turner
01757 630202
Main Street
Hemingbrough
Nr Selby
YO8 6QE
North Yorkshire

li & independent grocers

Holmesterne Farm Food Co Ltd

Holmesterne Foods has a proven history of success and innovation within the meat supply and added-value food business at national and regional levels and with multiple retailers.

Details

Steven Holden
01748 818283
Gatherley Road, Brompton on Swale, Richmond DL10 7JQ North Yorkshire
E: **steven.holden@holmesterne.com**

Did you know?

There's a tiny hamlet in Arkengarthdale, North Yorkshire, called Booze. It's up a hill with wonderful views but no pub.

Deli & independent grocers

Lewis & Cooper Ltd

LEWIS & COOPER

• PURVEYORS OF FINE FOOD AND WINE SINCE 1899 •

Long before buying locally became fashionable, Lewis & Cooper strove to bring to its shelves the best food and drink the region has to offer, complemented by the world's finest goods. More than 35,000 lines fill the store, which also boasts luxury hampers, gifts, china and a fine tea room.

Details

Kate Wintersgill
01609 772880
92 High Street
Northallerton
DL7 8PT
North Yorkshire
F: **01609 777933**
E: **sales@lewisandcooper.co.uk**
W: **www.lewisandcooper.co.uk**

Deli & independent grocers

LH Fine Foods

Opened in 2005 by Lucinda as a place where people can shop, enjoy illy coffee and homemade snacks in a relaxed atmosphere. Lucinda uses seasonal products, specialising in canapés, soups, pastries, readymade meals, party food, office lunches, English cheeses, freshly baked bread, chutneys, jams, luxury chocolates, and many more products.

Details

Lucinda Hyman
01423 506400
135 Otley Road, Harrogate
HG2 0AG North Yorkshire
E: **info@lucindahyman.co.uk**

Deli & independent grocers

Mackenzies Yorkshire Smokehouse

Mackenzies, established in 1985, is a family run business famous for award winning smoked and cured fish, meat, game and bacon. Browse the wide selection of products and giftware in our large shop and enjoy a fabulous breakfast, lunch or afternoon tea specially created for you by our award winning chef in our cafe/restaurant. The Smokehouse Art Gallery opens early summer 2009.

Details

Robert & Stella Crowson
01943 880369
Wood Nook Farm
Hardisty Hill
Blubberhouses
LS21 2PQ
North Yorkshire
F: **01943 880633**
E: **sales@yorkshiresmokehouse.co.uk**
W: **www.mackenziesyorkshire smokehouse.co.uk**

Deli & independent grocers

Proudfoot

Based in Scarborough, Proudfoot has a long history as an independent, family-run, grocery retailer. Throughout our three stores at Newby, Seamer and Eastfield we provide a unique service and shopping experience and offer strong support for sourcing regional Yorkshire products.

Details

Valerie Aston
01723 585960
Blinking Sike
Caxton Way
Eastfield Business Park
Scarborough
YO11 3YT
North Yorkshire
F: **01723 585959**
E: **valerie@proudfootgroup.com**
W: **www.proudfootgroup.com**

Deli & independent grocers

Weeton's

Over 3,000 square feet dedicated to the finest and freshest Yorkshire produce. You can watch the butchers and bakers at work in this state-of-the-art farm shop, listed by 'The Express' newspaper as one of the Top 100 shops in the world. The bustling cafe is also a popular meeting place.

Details

Andrew Loftus
01423 507100
23-24 West Park
Harrogate
HG1 1BJ
North Yorkshire
W: **www.weetons.com**

li & independent grocers

Yorkshire Dales Cheese Company

Specialist suppliers of hand crafted Yorkshire cheeses at markets and shows throughout the region. Creators of mouth watering cheese themed gifts and fabulous cheese wedding cakes. Contact us or visit our website and online shop for details on our superior cheese selection, mail order service and where to find us.

Details

David Harris and Jane Taylor
01325 243985
87 Swaledale Avenue
Darlington
DL3 9AR
County Durham
E: **info@yorkshiredalescheese.co.uk**
W: **www.yorkshiredalescheese.co.uk**

Deli & independent grocers

The Yorkshire Food Company

We are a modern, vibrant delicatessen and eatery in the heart of the city, priding ourselves on our extensive array of locally-sourced and speciality foods. Come and sample what we offer, spend time browsing or simply relax and enjoy a bite to eat or a drink.

Details

Kerry Brooks
07834 287077
130-134 Micklegate
York
YO1 6JX
North Yorkshire
E: **enquiries@theyorkshirefoodcompany.com**
W: **theyorkshirefoodcompany.com**

Farm shops

Ainsty Farms Direct

Farm shop with in-house butchery selling quality local beef, pork, lamb, poultry and game. The shop also houses a bakery producing a wide range of breads and pastries and an extensive deli.

Details

Lily Beaton
01423 331897
The Farm Shop, York Road
Green Hammerton York
YO26 8EQ North Yorkshire
F: **01423 331897**
E: **info@ainstyfarmshop.co.uk**

The Balloon Tree Farmshop & Café

The award winning Balloon Tree Farmshop is a great day out, with the shop selling a great choice of homegrown fruit and vegetables, rare breed meat, free range eggs, award-winning homemade cakes, chutneys and more.

Details

Will Machin
01759 373023
Stamford Bridge Road
Gate Helmsley, York
YO41 1NB North Yorkshire
F: **01759 373644**
E: **info@theballoontree.co.uk**
W: **theballoontree.co.uk**

Farm shops

Beadlam Grange

Farm shop and tearoom located in lovely surroundings and housed in a charming conversion on the farm. Includes an excellent butchers counter, fresh fruit and veg, cheeses and so much more, together with delicious home cooking in the delightful Granary Tearoom.

Details
Jenny Rooke
01439 770303
Nr. Helmsley,
York YO62 7TD
North Yorkshire
E: **info@beadlamgrange.co.uk**
W: **www.beadlamgrange.co.uk**

Bluebell Farm

Farm shop selling fresh produce, meat, game, pies and ready meals.

Details
Andrew Sykes
01904 798426
Broadlane Farm
Broadlane
Rufforth
YO23 3NJ
North Yorkshire
E: **apandje@hotmail.com**

Farm shops

Castle Howard Farm Shop

Castle Howard's Farm Shop features an excellent butcher's counter, with meat sourced from within a 15-mile radius, including estate-reared Aberdeen Angus and game. Other ranges include home-baked cakes, bread, chilled foods, grocery items plus wines and beers. Fresh fish available every Thursday.

Details
Rachel Jack
01653 648444
Castle Howard
York
YO60 7DA
North Yorkshire
F: **01653 648529**
E: **house@castlehoward.co.uk**
W: **www.castlehoward.co.uk**

Farm shops

Crimple Valley Fresh

A family run company based in Harrogate, specialising in home delivery of local produce, alongside our Ripley based shop offering local, quality produce. We also offer a chilled and ambient distribution service within the north of England for regional businesses.

Details
Steve Willis
01423 373636
Fulwith Mill Farm
Harrogate
HG2 8HJ
North Yorkshire
F: **01423 872200**
E: **sales@crimplevalleyfresh.com**
W: **www.crimplevalleyfresh.com**

m shops

odder

ɔdder is the flagship food ıop and café set up and ıampioned by the Yorkshire gricultural Society. Fodder sells ıe best Yorkshire food, made y Yorkshire people at Yorkshire alue-for-money prices. Fodder open 7 days a week from am-6pm Monday-Saturday ıd 10am-4pm Sunday.

etails

eborah Goodall
1423 546111
reat Yorkshire Showground
arrogate
G2 8NZ
orth Yorkshire
: **enquiries@fodderweb.co.uk**
/: **www.fodderweb.co.uk**

Farm shops

The Farmers Cart

Award-winning delicatessen and restaurant serving our own freshly picked home-grown fruits and vegetables, along with an array of Yorkshire cheeses and quiches. Our traditionally reared Aberdeen Angus beef, pork and lamb supply our newly opened butchery counter.

Details

Edward Sykes
01904 499183
Towthorpe Grange
Towthorpe Moor Lane
York YO32 9ST
North Yorkshire
F: **01904 491918**
E: info@thefarmerscart.co.uk
W: **www.thefarmerscartco.uk**

 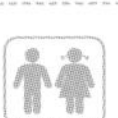 

Home Farm Shop

Delicious local produce, including home reared Aberdeen Angus beef, home baking, speciality breads and mouth-watering goodies. Already a popular addition to the York foodie scene.

Details

Lucy Jackson
01904 470562
Beningbrough Home Farm
Beningbrough
York
YO30 1DB
North Yorkshire
F: **01904 470001**
W: **www.homefarm-beningbrough.co.uk**

Farm shops

Hares Leap Delicatessen & Game Dealers

Hares Leap farm shop produces its own totally unique range of sausages, bacon and pies, pates, terrines, ready meals, breads and charcuterie and our own free range poultry and venison, with all game furred or feathered. We also showcase local arts and crafts.

Details

Kath and John Smith
01723 371607
Flatts Farm
Coastal Road Burniston
Scarborough
YO13 0DB
North Yorkshire
E: **shop@hares-leap.co.uk**
W: **www.hares-leap.co.uk**

Farm shops

Langlands Garden Centre

Established farm shop selling a range of produce including fresh fish, meat, veg, a range of confectionery, homemade cakes, freshly baked bread and dairy products.

Details

James Ducker
01430 873426
York Road, Shiptonthorpe
YO43 3PN North Yorkshire
F: **01430 871160**
W: **www.langlandsgardencentre.co.uk**

Mainsgill Farm Shop

Tea room and farm shop selling local produce including fruit and vegetables, chutneys, cakes, meats, cheeses and cooked meats.

Details

Maria Henshaw
01325 718860
Mainsgill Farm, East Layton
Richmond DL11 7PN
North Yorkshire

Farm shops

The Organic Pantry

The Organic Pantry is a family run organic farm based at Newton Kyme, growing over 50 different varieties of organic vegetables, which we sell via our comprehensive box scheme/delivery service, farm shop and website. We also supply other outlets/shops/restaurants through our wholesale business, but NO supermarkets.

Details

Fanny Watson
01937 531693
St. Helens Farm
Newton Kyme
Tadcaster
LS24 9LY
North Yorkshire
F: **01937 834062**
E: **fanny@theorganicpantry.co.uk**
W: **www.theorganicpantry.co.uk**

Farm shops

Quarton's Country Meats Farm Shop

We supply a range of quality meats at competitive prices from animals reared on the farm, including pork, beef, lamb, chicken, goose, turkey and duck. Fresh farm eggs are also available.

Details

Louise Quarton
01653 628249
Moor House Farm, Hovingham
York YO62 4LR, North Yorkshire
E: **louisequarton@aol.co.uk**
W: **www.quartonscountrymeats.com**

Did you know?

488,000

There are 488,000 pigs in the county – nearly two thirds of the English total.

Redcliffe Farm Shop & Café

Our deli-style farm shop offers a comprehensive selection of fresh meat, seasonal vegetables, eggs, dairy, Yorkshire cheeses, ice cream and locally made preserves. We produce home baked delicacies, pies and quiches. After shopping you can enjoy lunch, or coffee and cake in our cafe, with everything made on the premises.

Details

Martin Brown
01723 583194
Redcliffe Lane
Lebberston
Scarborough
YO11 3NT
North Yorkshire
F: **01723 583194**
E: **office@redcliffefarmshop.co.uk**
W: **www.redcliffefarmshop.co.uk**

Roots Farmshop & Cafe

Roots prides itself on a real farm retail experience and personal service. Our team of butchers are happy to talk you through the meat from field to fork. In the farm shop find out about the stories behind our wide range of local produce and relax in Roots Cafe with our delicious home-cooked food.

Details

Barry & Katherine Hutchinson
01609 882480
Home Farm
East Rounton
Northallerton
DL6 2LE
North Yorkshire
E: **info@rootsfarmshop.co.uk**
W: **rootsfarmshop.co.uk**

DISTRIBUTORS

Country Products Limited

Specialising in quality food products for the grocery, healthfood, delicatessen and farm shop trade. Soil Association registered and contract packers for some of the best known names in the industry.

Details

Mark Leather
01423 358858
Unit 6 Centre Park
Tockwith, York YO26 7QF
North Yorkshire
F: **01423 359858**
E: **sales@countryproducts.co.uk**
W: **www.countryproducts.co.uk**

GF Foods Ltd

Wholesale and distribute an extensive range of gluten and wheat free products including our own range "Brumby's". Brumby's is a range of savoury pastry products produced in North Yorkshire using only the finest, freshest, local ingredients.

Details

Sally Allister
01757 289207
Unit 5B
Blackwood Hall Business Park
North Duffield, Selby
YO8 5DD North Yorkshire
E: **sales@gfftrade.co.uk**
W: **www.gfftrade.co.uk**

East Yorkshire

East Yorkshire offers a real mix of experiences from spectacular countryside, to coastline and cities.

Hull is a vibrant waterfront city. Currently undergoing an urban renaissance, this is a changing city that manages to combine a vibrant mix of culture, shopping and nightlife with a rich maritime heritage. With an event calendar that features everything from jazz to sea shanties, there's plenty to enjoy not forgetting food flavours covering pies, preserves, and venison.

Close by is the beauty of the Yorkshire Wolds where you can take a ride along the award-winning Trans Pennine Cycle Trail, or the Yorkshire Wolds Way National Trail. Sample new routes linking the market towns of the Wolds, the churches of Holderness, and the wealth of sculpture at three magnificent stately homes or simply gaze out to sea from Flamborough's amazing white cliffs.

Further along discover the bright and breezy seaside resorts of Bridlington and Hornsea which are embedded in the stunning East Yorkshire coastline.

From city to countryside to coast, you'll find plenty of great value activities and accommodation in East Yorkshire.

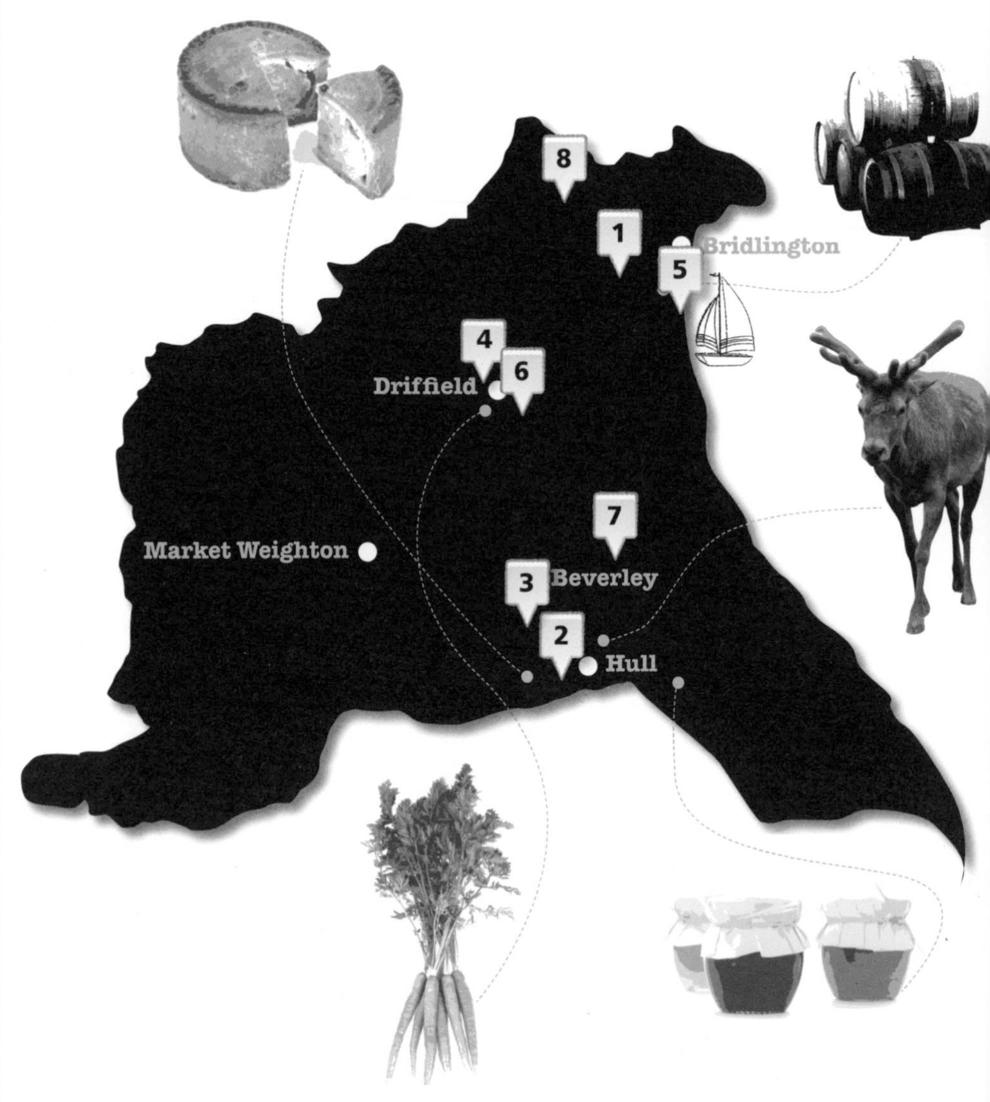
8
1
Bridlington
5
4
6
Driffield
7
Market Weighton
3
Beverley
2
Hull

Food Highlights

Bakers & confectioners

Kitchen

A family business producing beautiful breads, pretty pastries and 'Supa-dupa Meringues'. All sold at our delicious deli in Snaith and many shows throughout the region. We also supply 'Supa-dupa Meringues' to trade.

Details

Debbie Falkingham
01405 862662
10 Market Place, Snaith
Goole DN14 9HE
East Yorkshire

Shepcote Distributors Ltd

Manufacturer of cake decorations and marzipan confectionery. We also distribute sugar, syrups, nuts, seeds, pulses, cereals, dried fruit and confectionery to the bakery, ice cream and speciality trade.

Details

Richard Shepherdson
01377 252537
Pexton Road, Kelleythorpe Industrial Estate, Driffield YO25 9DJ East Yorkshire
E: **enquiries@shepcote.com**
W: **www.shepcote.com**

Bakers & confectioners

Side Oven Bakery

An award winning range of products are traditionally produced on our organic family farm on the edge of the Yorkshire Wolds including bread, flours, honey toasted mueslis, apple juice and cordials.

Details

Caroline Sellers
01262 488376
Carr House Farm
Foston-on-the-Wolds
Driffield YO25 8BS
East Yorkshire
W: **www.sideoven.com**

The Ultimate Candy Company Limited

Ultimate Candy's award winning hand-broken 16% butter fudge is but one of many products available within their range. For indulgence, Fairtrade, organic, and sugar free contact us now.

Details

Dave Richardson
01482 891754
4 Sheriff Highway
Hedon,
Hull
HU12 8HD
East Yorkshire
E: **ultimatecandy@aol.com**

Bakers & confectioners

White Rabbit Chocolate Company

White Rabbit Chocolate Company

We have created a unique range of delicious chocolate products for our region, using fine chocolate, fruits, nuts, spices, herbs, flowers, infusions and our Yorkshire honeycomb – all handmade and decorated with a little 'White Rabbit' magic! Group chocolate tastings and parties also available. Booking essential.

Details

Sally Hawkes
01482 679325
16 Dyer Lane
Beverley HU17 8AE
East Yorkshire
E: **whiterabbitchocolate@hotmail.co.uk**
W: **www.white-rabbit-chocolate.co.uk**

Beverages (alcoholic & non)

Blue Keld Springs Ltd

BLUE KELD
NATURAL MINERAL WATER

Blue Keld is a family run business based in the heart of the Yorkshire Wolds. Drawn from our natural artesian spring, the mineral water is high in calcium and low in sodium. We supply a range of natural and flavoured water, conference glass and our world renowned blue artesian glass bottles.

Details

Annabelle Marr
01377 271207
Throstle Nest
Cranswick
Driffield
YO25 9RE
East Yorkshire
E: **info@bluekeld.co.uk**
W: **www.bluekeld.co.uk**

Beverages (alcoholic & non)

Great Newsome Brewery Ltd

Situated on the East Yorkshire coast close to the City of Hull and run by the Hodgson family at Great Newsome Farm, the brewery produces award winning cask and bottled real ales, which are all named after local locations, words and dialects.

Details

Matthew Hodgson
01964 612201
Great Newsome Farm
South Frodingham
Winestead, Hull
HU12 0NR
East Yorkshire
F: **01964 612201**
E: **enquiries@greatnewsomebrewery.co.uk**
W: **www.greatnewsomebrewery.co.uk**

Beverages (alcoholic & non)

Wold Top Brewery

A small brewery situated high on the Yorkshire Wolds where gently sloping hills give way to the sea; part of Hunmanby Grange, family farm and home of the Mellor's. Award winning cask and bottled real ales made using traditional methods and home grown malting barley and pure chalk filtered water from the farm's borehole.

Details

Gill Mellor
01723 892222
Hunmanby Grange
Wold Newton
Driffield
YO25 3HS
East Yorkshire
F: **01723 892 229**
W: **www.woldtopbrewery.co.uk**

Dairy & eggs

Mr Moo's Real Dairy Ice Cream

Mr Moo's Dairy Ice Cream is a product that brings back memories of ice cream as it used to be. Its simple, rich, creamy flavour uses milk from the family farm and where possible, locally sourced ingredients.

Details

Stephen Forman
01262 469829
Southfield House Farm
Skipsea, Driffield
YO25 8SY East Yorkshire
F: **01262 468209**
E: **info@mrmoos.co.uk**
W: **www.mrmoos.co.uk**

Fish (fresh & smoked)

Crooks Fish

We provide the nation with fresh Whitby fish and seafood delivered straight to the customer's home or workplace ordered via our online fishmongers shop.

Details

William Crooks
01947 605677
Dennis Crooks Wholesale Fish
Whitby Business Park
Whitby YO22 4PU
East Yorkshire
E: **info@crooksfish.co.uk**
W: **www.crooksfish.co.uk**

Fresh ingredients

Scholes Limited

Growers, packers and distributors of potatoes, squash and pumpkin. A family owned/managed business farming circa 2,500ha on the Yorkshire Wolds. Supplying retail, catering and wholesale sectors.

Details

Mark Southwell
01377 256710
Green Lane Farm
Nafferton, Driffield
YO25 4LF East Yorkshire
E: **mark.southwell@scholes-ltd.co.uk**
W: **www.scholes-ltd.co.uk**

Did you know?

There are **1,139,348** lambs in Yorkshire (over a seventh of the English total)

Ocean Rewards

A family business, licensed to catch wild sea bass and salmon and processors of fresh crabs – boiled on our premises daily. Awarded MSC accreditation 2008. Suppliers to public and trade, enquiries welcome.

Details

Karen Sanderson
07716 120462
64 Hilderthorpe Rd
Bridlington
YO15 3BQ
E: **froudy32@hotmail.com**

W Clappison Ltd

Clappison's of Risby produce the finest brussel sprouts in Yorkshire. Supplied fresh to both public and trade, from October through to March.

Details

John Clappison
01482 848132
Beverley
HU17 8SS
East Yorkshire
E: **john@risby.karoo.co.uk**

Aarhus Karlshamn

Aarhus Karlshamn (AAK) is a leading supplier of speciality fats and oils. The company has the broadest product range in the industry and is second to none in the ability to offer cost efficient, added value solutions to customers in the food, confectionery and cosmetics industries.

Details

Rachel Neale
01482 586747
King George Dock
Hull
HU9 5PX
East Yorkshire
F: **01482 709447**
W: **www.aak.com**

Anna's Happy Trotters Yorkshire Free Range Pork

Our pigs enjoy a free range lifestyle from beginning to end. Being part of only 2% of pigs reared in this way in the UK they are undoubtedly lucky, well looked after pigs. And just like their quality of life, the quality of meat from our pigs is second to none.

Details

Anna Longthorp
01430 433030
Burland
Holme Road
Howden DN14 7LY
East Yorkshire
F: **01430 432138**
E: **anna@longthorp.com**

Meat, poultry & game (fresh & smoked)

Burdass Lamb Ltd

Home produced lamb which comes from a flock that has taken the Burdass family over 80 years to produce. Traditionally reared sheep.

Details

Ian Burdass
01262 490271
3 Moorcroft Cottages
Harpham Driffield
YO25 4QY
East Yorkshire
E: **burdaz3@aol.com**

Burton's of Wilberfoss

Burtons of Wilberfoss produce the highest quality pork sausages and dry cured bacon from our own herd of free range pigs, ensuring full traceability.

Details

Grant Burton
01759 380244
Manor House Farm
Wilberfoss
York
YO41 5NY

Meat, poultry & game (fresh & smoked)

Paynes Turkeys

A family-run farming business, rearing turkeys since 1953. We produce day-old turkey poults, growing turkeys and traditional farm fresh barn-reared white and bronze turkeys for Christmas.

Details

Christopher Payne
07916 174068
East Bursea Farm
Holme on Spalding Moor
YO43 4DB
East Yorkshire
E: **sales@paynesturkeys.co.uk**

Rose Cottage Foods

We produce speciality hand-made savoury pies. They are made using the finest local ingredients. Our products are sold at farmers markets, food festivals and shows throughout Yorkshire.

Details

Rupert Clemmit
01377 257700
Main Street
Garton on the Wolds
Driffield
YO25 3ET
East Yorkshire

Meat, poultry & game (fresh & smoked)

Sledmere Estate

Venison produced from own herd on the Sledmere Estate.

Details

Stephen Greenfield
01377 236221
Sledmere Estate Office
Driffield, YO25 3XG
East Yorkshire
F: **01377 236560**
E: **stephengreenfield@sledmere-estate.com**

Yorkshire Outdoor Pork Company Ltd

Yorkshire Outdoor supply speciality sausage, bacon and fresh pork products, traditionally made, available for local consumers through a variety of retail outlets. We provide quality produce of known provenance using only outdoor reared pork.

Details

Mark Burton
01482 337990.
Malmo Park
Malmo Road
Sutton Fields, Hull
HU7 0YH
East Yorkshire

Prepared food

William Jackson Food Group

WILLIAM JACKSON FOOD GROUP

William Jackson Food Group is a fifth generation family business (established 1851) comprising five manufacturing divisions: Aunt Bessie's (traditional frozen food), Hazeldene (prepared salads), Jackson's Bakery (sandwich/speciality breads), Kwoks (chilled oriental convenience meals) and Parripak (prepared vegetables). The Group also owns the Ferguson Fawsitt Arms, a traditional pub/restaurant with 10 rooms near Beverley.

Details

Di Kirby
01482 224939
The Riverside Building
Livingstone Road
Hessle
HU13 0DZ
East Yorkshire
F: **01482 223217**
E: **djk@wjs.co.uk**
W: **www.wjs.co.uk**

eserves, honey, condiments & spices

Gold From The Wold Ltd

Gold from the Wold's cold-pressed rapeseed oil is simply pressed once and allowed to settle naturally on the farm, just down the road from the fields (on the Yorkshire Wolds) where it was grown by Paul. It's an entirely natural product and is great for all culinary uses. Enjoy!

Details

Paul Jackson
01262 672293
Carnaby House Farm
Carnaby, Bridlington
YO16 4UJ
East Yorkshire
E: **info@goldfromthewold.co.uk**
W: **www.goldfromthewold.co.uk**

Preserves, honey, condiments & spices

Kitchen Guru

Kitchen Guru produces the most innovative spice kits to make fresh, authentic Indian meals at home. 20 delicious recipes available.

Details

Chandra Parmar
01482 864799
Petunia House, Petunia
Lakeside Park
Plaxton Bridge Road
Woodmansey, Nr Beverley
HU17 0RT East Yorkshire
E: **info@kitchenguru.co.uk**
W: **www.kitchenguru.co.uk**

Prepared food

Yorkshire Hemp Limited

Yorkshire Hemp Ltd provide both certified organic and conventional hemp food seeds, shelled hemp seeds, hemp oil, hemp flour, hemp sauce and the essential oil of hemp to the baking, food manufacturing and nutraceutical industry. Yorkshire Hemp's own branded products are available in retail outlets, through wholesale or direct.

Details

Paul Jenkinson
01377 272790
Twydale Business Park
Unit 8b, Skerne Road
Driffield YO25 6JX
East Yorkshire
F: **01377 250671**
E: **sales@hempmarket.com**
W: **www.yorkshirehemp.com**
W: **www.hempmarket.com**

Prepared food

Natural Sports Nutrition

Performance-Meals meet the high nutritional demands of athletes involved in training for sports and fitness. Providing a unique ratio of nutrients supporting lean muscle development and enhanced sports performance.

Details

Mike Webb
02081 233074
The Enterprise Centre
Cottingham Road, Hull
HU6 7RX
East Yorkshire
E: **mikewebb@performancemeals.com**
W: **www.performancemeals.com**

Deli & independent grocers

Chucks & Cheese

We are a deli, farm shop and online shop specialising in English and Continental cheeses, preserves, chutneys, ice cream, diabetic and gluten free products, olives and fresh fruit and veg.

Details

Zoe Bayston
01405 768748
79 Pasture Road
Goole DN14 6BP
East Yorkshire
F: **01405 862532**
E: **chucksncheese@yahoo.co.uk**
W: **www.chucksandcheese.co.uk**

Farm shops

Burton Agnes Hall Farmer's Food Store

Farmer's Food Store open daily with a fantastic range of locally produced, fresh, seasonal produce; including poultry, pork, beef and lamb, fruit and veg, smoked foods, goats' and cows' cheeses, cakes and biscuits, puddings, soups, preserves and much more.

Details

Natasha Taylor
01262 490324
Burton Agnes Hall Courtyard
Burton Agnes
Driffield
YO25 4NB
East Yorkshire
F: **01262 490678**
E: **office@burtonagnes.com**
W: **www.burtonagnes.com**

Farm shops

Drewtons Farm Shop

Scheduled to open in November 2010. Farm shop, butchery, bakery, fresh fish, cheeses, deli, wines, fruit and veg, café and courtyard dining. Aberdeen Angus beef and game from The Drewton Estate. www.bygeorgeitsscrummy.co.uk

Details
Katie Taylor
07974 375432
Kettlethorpe Farm, The Drewton Estate, South Cave
Brough HU15 2AG
East Riding of Yorkshire
E: **katie@drewtons.co.uk**
W: **www.drewtons.co.uk**

Did you know?

Yorkshire Pudding was first referred to in a cookery book in 1747 - The Art of Cookery Made Plain and Easy by Hannah Glasse. "It is an exceeding good pudding, the gravy of the meat eats well with it," she said.

rm shops

Kelleythorpe Farm Shop

We specialise in tender, well hung, homebred Aberdeen Angus beef finished traditionally with no additives. Our Angus burgers are legendary. We also sell a full butchery range of local meats, local vegetables and fruit in season, home baked pies, cakes and puddings and a good range of English cheeses, freshly prepared sandwiches and other local products.

Details

Tiffy Hopper
01377 256627
Kelleythorpe
Driffield
YO25 9DW
East Yorkshire
F: **01377 232956**
E: **hoppertiffy@hotmail.com**

Farm shops

Manor Farm Shop

Selling the best of locally produced food, including fruit and veg, jams, pickles, baking, cooked meats, bacon, fish, sandwiches, milk, eggs, poultry, ice-cream and over thirty English cheeses.

Details

Adrian Fry
01377 271038
Manor Farm
Hutton Cranswick
Driffield YO25 9PQ
East Yorkshire
F: **01377 271 038**
W: **www.manorfarmshop.com**

Sands Lane Nurseries Ltd

A 2.5 acre site with superb quality pick your own soft fruits grown under glass, farm and coffee shop selling our own and local produce, well stocked plant nursery grown by ourselves, plus animal petting area.

Details

Sue Badham
01430 423131
Sand Lane, South Cave
Hull, HU15 2JQ
East Yorkshire
E: **sue.sandslanenurseries@hotmail.com**

HOSPITALITY

Café & Tearoom

Millers Tea Room & Farm Shop

Set in beautiful rural countryside, Millers offers a relaxed and friendly atmosphere. Meals are prepared on the premises using fresh local produce. We bake a wide selection of homemade cakes and pastries. The farm shop sells locally sourced vegetables, cheeses, meat, wines, beers and a selection of unusual gifts.

Details

Elane Townend
01482 631702
Raywell Lodge Park, Riplingham Road, Raywell HU16 5YL
East Riding of Yorkshire
E: **etownend@etownend.karoo.co.uk**
W: **www.millerstearoomandfarmshop.co.uk**

Hotels & restaurants

Artisan Restaurant

Yorkshire Life Restaurant of the Year 2009, Top 100 UK Restaurant 2008/9, Top 40 UK Restaurant outside London, Michelin/Good Food listed. The restaurant is set within a Georgian townhouse, seats up to 16 guests and is owned and run by husband and wife Richard and Lindsey. Lovingly prepared food in an intimate setting.

Details

Richard & Lindsey Johns
01482 644906
22 The Weir, Hessle
HU13 0RU
East Yorkshire
E: **eat@artisanrestaurant.com**
W: **www.artisanrestaurant.com**

Hotels & restaurants

Boars Nest

BOARS NEST

Our classic British restaurant, in an empathetic conversion of an Edwardian butchers shop, is perfect for a light lunch, evening dining or a relaxing beer, glass of wine or champagne, in our first floor lounge bar.

Details

Dina Hanchett
01482 445577

22 Princes Avenue
Hull HU5 3QA
East Yorkshire
E: **boarsnest@boarsnest.karoo.co.uk**
W: **www.boarsnesthull.com**

Hotels & restaurants

Boothferry Road Community Project

The Courtyard, from Boothferry Road Community Project, presents an innovative combination of outstanding facilities, which are available to everyone at reasonable cost. The project has a vital role in supporting and developing local community and voluntary action in Goole.

Details

Linda Thornton
01405 837100
Boothferry Road
Goole DN14 6AE
East Yorkshire

Did you know?

The village of Denby Dale near Huddersfield has been famously making giant pies for more than 220 years, including to celebrate the victory of the Duke of Wellington over Napoleon at the Battle of Waterloo.

Hotels & restaurants

Fudge Café-Restaurant Ltd

Fudge is a little slice of foodie heaven located in Hull's cosmopolitan Princes Avenue, where the welcome is guaranteed to be warm and friendly. With a brasserie menu that offers luscious treats from brunch to dinner, Fudge Café-Restaurant creates a vibrant atmosphere in which to enjoy contemporary cuisine.

Details

Rosie Goodman
01482 441019
93 Princes Avenue
Hull HU5 3QP
East Yorkshire
E: **info@fudgecafe-restaurant.com**
W: **www.fudgecafe-restaurant.com**

Hotels & restaurants

The Pipe and Glass Inn

Award winning 18 century country Inn situated in the heart of East Yorkshire. Snug bar and stylish restaurant area, serving modern British food with East Riding accent, wide range of Yorkshire real ales and bespoke wine list.

Details

James Mackenzie
01430 810246
West End, South Dalton,
Beverley
HU17 7PN
East Yorkshire
E: **email@pipeandglass.co.uk**
W: **www.pipeandglass.co.uk**

Did you know?

World-renowned British retailer Marks and Spencer started as a stall at Kirkgate Market, Leeds in 1884. The first stall is marked today with a green and gold commemorative clock.

Hotels & restaurants

Rags Restaurant with Rooms

Rags
HOTEL, BAR & RESTAURANT

Rags is situated on the harbour edge with fabulous views of the South Bay. Serving locally sourced produce from Bridlington crab and seabass to homemade soup and chutneys. Our varied menu has something to suit every taste. Open all day for food and drink. We also provide en-suite accommodation.

Details

Julie Dyl
01262 400355
South Pier
Bridlington
YO15 3AN
East Yorkshire
E: **ragshotel@tesco.net**
W: **www.ragshotel.co.uk**

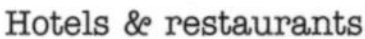

Hotels & restaurants

Reedness Hall Cottage

A tranquil cottage, all on one level, in a rural village and within riverbank walking distance of the RSPB Blacktoft sands. A complementary deliciouslyyorkshire welcome pack to help you unwind, with locally sourced produce, homemade preserves, and free range eggs from our happy hens.

Details

Kate Andrews
01405 704555
Reedness
Nr Goole DN14 8ER
East Riding of Yorkshire
F: **01405 704555**
E: **enquiries@reednesshall.co.uk**
W: **www.reednesshall.co.uk**

Hotels & restaurants

Tickton Grange

We have a real Yorkshire Passion which is reflected in the ingredients we use to create our seasonal menus. In the East Riding we have a wealth of quality produce that allows our chefs to develop exciting vibrant dishes for today's discerning diners. Restaurant, hotel, conferences, weddings and all other occasions.

Details

David Nowell
01964 543666
Main Street
Tickton, Beverley
HU17 9SH
East Yorkshire
F: **01964 542556**
E: **info@ticktongrange.co.uk**
W: **www.beverleyticktongrange.co.uk**

Hider Food Imports Ltd

A family owned company, specialising in quality food, be that nuts and dried fruits or the very best delicatessen products from around the world. Local, continental, organic, Fairtrade, gluten-free… and much more in stock. We cover the country with our own fleet of lorries, giving a friendly, weekly delivery service supplying the best confectionery, cakes, biscuits and fruit available to man.

Details

Duncan Hider
01482 561137
Wiltshire Road
Kingston upon Hull
HU4 6PA
East Yorkshire
F: **01482 565 668**
E: **sales@hiderfoods.co.uk**
W: **www.hiderfoods.co.uk**

South Yorkshire

Conisbrough Castle

South Yorkshire encompasses Sheffield, Rotherham, Doncaster and Barnsley, and has an abundance of heritage, gardens and open spaces, bustling nightlife and cultural events, sports and outdoor activities along with traditional rural villages and market towns.

It doesn't matter if you have a few hours or a few days to spend in the South Yorkshire region, you'll find lots of inspiring ideas and new places to visit.

If you enjoy the outdoors, South Yorkshire offers a gateway to the Peak District National Park. It is also home to award-winning galleries, live comedy clubs, nightclubs and music venues.

From the oldest classic horse race in the world, the St Leger, to world championship snooker, South Yorkshire also has an enviable programme of world class events with a richness of food in its locally-produced beers, bakeries and confectionery. And it's also a fun place to be: take to the slopes at Sheffield Ski Village, enjoy water sports at Rother

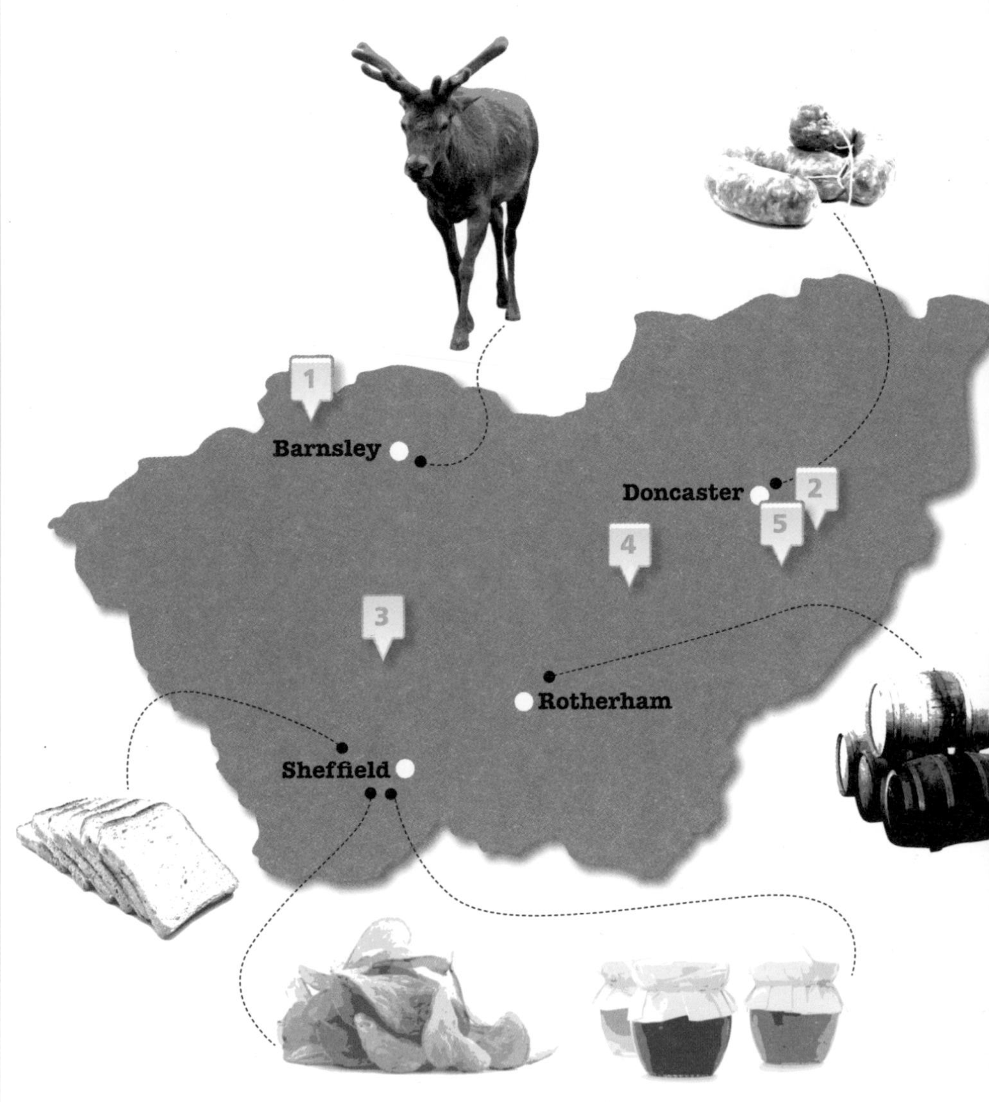
1
Barnsley
Doncaster
2
5
4
3
Rotherham
Sheffield

Food Highlights

1. Cannon Hall Farm Shop *(see entry on page 162)*
2. Mount Pleasant Hotel *(see entry on page 159)*
3. Round Green Venison *(see entry on page 154)*
4. The Cadeby Inn *(see entry on page 158)*
5. The Crown at Bawtry *(see entry on page 159)*

Bakers & confectioners

A. L. Simpkin & Co Ltd

Simpkins have been pioneers of high grade glucose confectionery since 1921. All still produced by traditional methods and recipes and incorporating only natural colours and flavours. Brands – Simpkins Travel Tins, Nipits, Candy. Vast Sugar Free and NAFNAC product portfolio.

Details

Karen Simpkin
0114 2348736
Hunter Road
Sheffield
S6 4LD
South Yorkshire
F: **0114 232 5635**
E: **sales@alsimpkin.com**
W: **www.alsimpkin.com**

Bakers & confectioners

Cooplands (Doncaster) Ltd

One of Yorkshire's leading family bakers with over 76 shops throughout the region. We achieved BRC accreditation at the end of 2008 and now offer proven high quality bakery products to the wholesale market alongside the production of frozen raw pastry for bake off using our state of the art Rondo pastry make up line.

Details

Robert McIllroy
01302 361333
Victoria Mill Business Park
Wharf Road
Wheatley
Doncaster
DN1 2SX
South Yorkshire
F: **01302 329776**
E: **customer.service@cooplands.co.uk**
W: **www.cooplands.co.uk**

Bakers & confectioners

Foster's Bakery Ltd

Based in South Yorkshire, Fosters are ideally placed to serve local and national retailers and caterers with premium quality bread morning goods and confectionery.

Details

John Foster
01226 382877
Towngate Mapplewell
Barnsley S75 6AS
South Yorkshire
F: **01226 390087**
E: **jrf@fostersbakery.co.uk**
W: **www.bake-it.com**

Maxons Ltd

Manufacturers of old fashioned hard boiled sweets including Yorkshire Mixture and fruit rock. Extensive product range, packaged in large weigh-out jars, small tins, pre-pack bags or bulk bags.

Details

Chris Pitchfork
0114 2554216
Bradbury Street
Sheffield
S8 9QQ
South Yorkshire
F: **0114 250 9683**
W: **www.maxons.co.uk**

akers & confectioners

Opera Desserts

Italian influenced Opera Desserts is a producer of fine quality desserts and ice-cream. The desserts are made using locally sourced and produced ingredients, with sugar and fat free products available. Suppliers to restaurants, hotels and smaller retail outlets as well as direct to consumer.

Details

Angela Lombardo
01302 769699
42/43 Waterdale
Doncaster
DN1 3EY
South Yorkshire
E: **operadesserts@opera-restaurant.co.uk**

Bakers & confectioners

Potts Bakers Ltd

Potts Bakers are Barnsley's oldest bakers, established in 1891 and currently run by the 4th and 5th generation of Potts. We have 4 shops locally in the Barnsley area, and also supply wholesale to local retailers and sandwich shops. Potts have ability to package label and barcode products if required. We also contract bake for regional and national markets.

Details

Roger Potts
01226 249175
Stanley Road
Stairfoot
Barnsley
S70 3PG
South Yorkshire
F: **01226 249175**
E: **roger@pottsbakers.co.uk**
W: **www.pottsbakers.co.uk**

Beverages (alcoholic & non)

Cafeology Ltd

Cafeology are an independently owned, exclusively Fairtrade, beverage company based in South Yorkshire. We specialise in the supply of the finest Fairtrade coffee, tea, hot chocolate and iced coffee, supplying both food service and retail markets throughout the UK.

Details

Bryan Unkles
0870 0119441
7 Meersbrook
Enterprise Centre
Valley Road
Sheffield
S8 9FT
South Yorkshire
F: **0870 011 4632**
E: **info@cafeology.com**
W: **www.cafeology.com**

Dairy & Eggs

Amos Kaye & Son

FRESH EGGS DIRECT FROM OUR FARM
Amos Kaye & Son
Townhead Farm, Dunford Bridge
Nr. Sheffield S36 4TG
Tel: Barnsley 01226 763134

Amos Kaye & Son is a family business producing quality eggs from our own farm. Delivering to many areas. Suppliers to all types of businesses including restaurants, cafes, public houses, nursing homes, etc. Competitive prices and quality guaranteed.

Details

William Kaye
01439 766 825
Townhead Farm
Dunford Bridge
Sheffield
S36 4TG
South Yorkshire

Fish (fresh & smoked)

Bingham's Food Ltd

Bingham's Food manufactures and sells a fresh range of meat and fish spreads to the retail and food service sectors. Bingham's spreads are ideal on sandwiches, bread rolls, toast or crackers.

Details

Paul Singleton
0114 2661676
148 Western Road
Sheffield S10 1LD
South Yorkshire
E: **peter.moon@binghamsfoods.co.uk**
W: **www.binghamsfood.co.uk**

Did you know?

Wensleydale cheese was first made by French Cistercian monks who settled at Fors in 1150. Real Yorkshire Wensleydale is still made today at the Wensleydale Creamery in Hawes.

Fresh Ingredients

G W Price Ltd

Wholesale fruit and potato merchants and importers. Prepared fruit and vegetable specialists.

Details

Debra Willoughby
01246 432818
13 High Street
Eckington
Sheffield
S21 4DH
South Yorkshire
E: **debra@gwprice.co.uk**
W: **www.gwprice.co.uk**

Fresh Ingredients

Netherthorpe Fresh Produce

Wholesale suppliers of fresh fruit, vegetables, salads and dairy products to the catering trade.

Details

Nigel Jacobs

0114 287 8789

York House
Ulley Lane
Aston, Sheffield S26 2DR
South Yorkshire
E: **nicesprouts@hotmail.com**

Simply Onions Ltd

Specialising in prepared English onions, whole, peeled, sliced or diced for food manufacturers.

Details

Nigel Jacobs

0114 2878789

Ulley Lane, Aston
Sheffield S26 2DR
South Yorkshire
E: **simplyonions@hotmail.co.uk**

Meat, poultry & game (fresh & smoked)

John Crawshaw Butchers for Food Lovers

This well established business has become an institution for many of its retail and trade customers. Finest quality beef, pork and lamb selected and sourced from local farms within 30 miles of the business.

Details

John Crawshaw

0114 288 3548

518-524 Manchester Road
Stocksbridge, Sheffield
S36 2DW South Yorkshire
F: **0114 288 2020**
E: **info@johncrawshaws.co.uk**
W: **www.johncrawshaws.co.uk**

Did you know?

15%

More than 15% of all England's potatoes are produced in the region.

Meat, poultry & game (fresh & smoked)

Northern Catering Butchers Ltd

Northern Catering are specialists in supplying high quality, fresh meat products to the catering industry. An expansive product range reflects expertise and knowledge in supplying the finest quality fresh meat products across a diverse species range, which takes into account seasonality and ever changing industry trends.

Details

Lee Allsop

01709 789135

Unit 3 Ashley Industrial Estate
Rawmarsh Road
Rotherham
S60 1RU
South Yorkshire
F: **01709 789139**
E: **sales@northern-catering.co.uk**
W: **www.northern-catering.com**

Round Green Venison Company

Now in our 30th year of deer farming, from our own EU approved plant we supply the public and trade with a range of venison – joints and steaks to pies and pate.

Details

Richard Elmhirst

01226 205577

Round Green Farm

Worsbrough, Barnsley

S75 3DR South Yorkshire

F: **01226 281294**

E: **info@roundgreenfarm.co.uk**

W: **www.roundgreenfarm.co.uk**

Pies

Topping Pie Company

The Topping Pie Company are manufacturers of speciality gold award winning pork pies and quiches. A total of 21 gold awards have been received by Toppings during the last 8 years.

Details

Roger Topping

01302 738333

Unit 2 Chappell Drive

Waterside Ind Estate

Doncaster DN1 2RF

South Yorkshire

F: **01302 738366**

E: **mail@toppingspies.co.uk**

Prepared Food

King Asia Foods Ltd

King Asia Foods are the leading manufacturers of oriental food in the frozen food industry. Our 50,000 sq ft factory produces over 15 million meals a year. We pride ourselves on providing the highest quality oriental food solutions for food service and retail markets.

Details

Dan Suh

01302 760070

Middle Bank

Doncaster DN4 5JJ

South Yorkshire

F: **01302 760386**

E: **dansuh@kingasia.co.uk**

W: **www.kingasia.co.uk**

Pies

The Curry Pasty Company

The Curry Pasty Company provides high quality handmade products. Our meat and vegetarian ranges use traditional herbs and spices, giving a deliciously unique and tantalizing taste that captures the appetite.

Details

Wendy Wilson

07904 094231

141 Sheffield Road

Warmsworth Doncaster

DN4 9QX South Yorkshire

E: **info@thecurrypastycompany.co.uk**

Prepared Food

Inspired Eating

Festive fine food hampers specialising in Yorkshire products.

Details

Jon & Debbie Broadhurst

0114 2353569

94 Busheywood Road

Dore, Sheffield

S17 3QD South Yorkshire

E: **sales@inspiredeating.co.uk**

W: **www.inspiredeating.co.uk**

The Real Yorkshire Pudding Co Ltd

The Real Yorkshire Pudding company produce fresh and frozen pre baked Yorkshire puddings using only the finest fresh ingredients.

Details

Deidre Bailey

01405 815523

Coulman Road Industrial Estate, Thorne, Doncaster

DN8 5JS

F: **01405 817710**

E: **dbailey@realyorks.co.uk**

W: **www.realyorks.co.uk**

Yorkshire Crisp Company

Yorkshire Crisps – your local hand-made crisp producer. Made with local produce and completely natural flavourings, not a preservative or trace of MSG in sight! Presented in unique and attractive packaging and available in 100g barrels, 50g bags and 500g catering packs in ten mouth-watering flavours.

Details

Tim Wheatley
01909 774411
2A Waleswood Ind Estate
Wales Bar
Sheffield
S26 5PY
South Yorkshire
F: **01909 773366**
E: **timwheatley@yorkshirecrisps.co.uk**
W: **www.yorkshirecrisps.co.uk**

Catherine's Choice

Producers of bespoke Great Taste Award winning preserves, fruit curds, fruit butters and sauces. All of our products are additive and gluten free. Ingredients are sourced as locally as possible. Products are available to both retail and catering outlets.

Details

David Trickett
07836 345858
59 Westbourne Road
Broomhill
Sheffield
S10 2QT
South Yorkshire
F: **08707 058 856**
E: **sales@catherines-choice.com**
W: **www.catherines-choice.com**

Glenroyd Organics

Homemade organic preserves, chutneys and condiments certified by the Soil Association. Available in various sizes for independent retail, gift hampers and catering.

Details

Michelle Roper-Shaw
01226 730809
208 Dodworth Road
Barnsley S70 6PF
South Yorkshire
E: **info@glenroydorganics.co.uk**
W: **www.glenroydorganics.co.uk**

Womersley Fine Foods

The Womersley brand was launched from Womersley Hall in 1979, and has become one of Yorkshire's and England's leading gourmet brands for fruit vinegars, dressings and jellies, also a new range of marinated olives. Products now available in food service size containers.

Details

Glynne Smith
01977 620294
Garden Cottage Park Lane
Doncaster DN6 9BH
South Yorkshire
E: **glynne.smith1@btinternet.com**
W: **www.womersleyfinefoods.co.uk**

Cafe & tearoom

Cello Coffee House

A cosy little coffee shop in the heart of Greenhill Village on the edge of Derbyshire.

Details

Liz Austin
0114 237 7991
212 Bocking Lane, Greenhill
Sheffield S8 7BP
South Yorkshire
W: **www.cellocoffeehouse.co.uk**

Did you know?

Yorkshire Pudding was first referred to in a cookery book in 1747 – The Art of Cookery Made Plain and Easy by Hannah Glasse. "It is an exceeding good pudding, the gravy of the meat eats well with it," she said.

Cafe & tearoom

Yorkshire Wildlife Park Limited

After exciting encounters with animals, visitors to Yorkshire Wildlife Park can enjoy a flavour of Yorkshire at the Wild Café. Mr Toppings pies from Doncaster, local Wilkinson's sausages and more and a selection of traditional Yorkshire cakes to finish!

Details

Sandra Harper
01302 535057
Brockholes Lane
Branton, Doncaster
DN3 3NH South Yorkshire
F: **01302 533187**
E: **info@yorkshirewildlifepark.co.uk**
W: **www.yorkshirewildlifepark.co.uk**

Hotels & restaurants

Artisan of Sheffield

Modern British cooking showcasing classical innovation at its finest. Continues to be the city's highest rated eatery and restaurant of choice 15 years after it first opened.

Details

Simon Webster
0114 2666096
32-44 Sandygate Road
Crosspool
Sheffield
S10 5RY
South Yorkshire
W: **www.relaxeatanddrink.com**

tels & restaurants

Aston Hall (Tomahawk Group)

A stunning luxury country house hotel set in 55 acres of gardens and meadowland. Situated one mile from the MI and, therefore, a perfect focal point for meeting friends and relatives for celebrations or a superb dinner. The restaurant excels in creating interesting menus featuring various fresh local Yorkshire produce.

Details

Claire Sutherland and Raquel Silva
0114 2872309
Worksop Road
Aston
Sheffield
S26 2EE
South Yorkshire
F: **0114 287 3228**
E: **reservations@astonhallhotel.co.uk**
W: **www.tomahawkhotels.co.uk**

Hotels & restaurants

The Best Western Cutlers Hotel

We are Sheffield's only independently owned boutique hotel, closely situated near Sheffield theatres and all that Sheffield City Centre has to offer.

Details

James Hague
0114 2739939
George Street
Sheffield, S1 2PF
South Yorkshire
F: **0114 2768332**
E: **james@cutlershotel.co.uk**
W: **www.cutlershotel.co.uk**

Did you know?

There's a tiny hamlet in Arkengarthdale, North Yorkshire, called Booze. It's up a hill with wonderful views but no pub.

Hotels & restaurants

The Best Western Pastures Hotel

Ideally located for business or pleasure, The Best Western Pastures Hotel offers excellent ensuite accommodation at exceptional value for money. Reeds Restaurant set in stunning surroundings and situated in the hotel is fast gaining a reputation for superb food and service, using only the finest locally sourced produce and suppliers.

Details

Janet Scott
01709 577707
Pastures Road
Rotherham
S64 0JJ
South Yorkshire
E: **info@pastureshotel.co.uk**
W: **www.pastureshotel.co.uk**

Hotels & restaurants

Brooklands Hotel

Barnsley's award winning 4-star hotel, restaurant and conference centre. 77 bedrooms and 9 conference rooms catering for up to 400 people, Brooklands invites you to enjoy superb service, gracious surroundings and absolute comfort. In the heart of Yorkshire and situated on the fringes of the Pennines, perfect for business or pleasure.

Details

Karen Tyas
01226 299571
Barnsley Road
Dodworth
Barnsley
S75 3JT
South Yorkshire
E: **karen@brooklandshotel.com**
W: **www.brooklandshotel.com**

Hotels & restaurants

The Cadeby Inn

The Cadeby Inn is a stylish 18th century country pub serving modern British food. It's a free house and has an ever changing offering of real cask ales, a large selection of malt whiskies and a superb wine list. We have lovely dining areas, blazing fires in winter and an apple orchard garden in summer. The Old Granary provides state of the art conference facilities and is a charming venue for weddings, christenings or private parties.

Details

Barbara Kirking
01709 864009
Main Street
Cadeby
Doncaster
DN5 7SW
South Yorkshire
E: **info@cadebyinn.co.uk**
W: **www.cadebyinn.co.uk**

Hotels & restaurants

Canteen

Canteen

Fast paced diner offering fixed price menus. All food cooked fresh in front of you. Good food, great value!

Details

Simon Wild
0114 266 6096
32-44 Sandygate Road
Crosspool
Sheffield
S10 5RY
South Yorkshire
W: **www.relaxeatanddrink.com**

he Cricket Inn

onic Sheffield Pub, which in its ost recent guise has gained a umber of awards including Pub f The Year 2008. Situated on the oundary line of the Totley Cricket itch on Penny Lane. Sitting on e edge of the Peak District it as the feel of a great country ub but is only minutes from himney pots!?

etails
ack Baker
114 2365256
enny Lane
otley
heffield
17 3AZ
outh Yorkshire
: **enquiries@brewkitchen.co.uk**
: **www.cricketinn.co.uk**

The Crown Hotel (Bawtry)

A chic, rustic, contemporary retreat, offering some of the best accommodation in South Yorkshire, serving locally sourced food and our famous "Yorkshire Tapas" menu.

Details
Craig Dowie
01302 710341
Market Place, Bawtry
Doncaster DN10 6JW
South Yorkshire
F: **01302 711798**
E: **reservations@crownhotel-bawtry.com**
W: **www.crownhotel-bawtry.com**

The Grand St Ledger Hotel

The Hotel is conveniently located just outside central Doncaster and provides the ideal location when visiting Doncaster whilst on business or for pleasure.

Details
Paula Beeby
01302 364111
Bennetthorpe
Doncaster
DN2 6AX
South Yorkshire
F: **01302 329865**
E: **sales@grandstleger.com**

Mount Pleasant Hotel

Mount Pleasant is a 4-star country hotel, set in 100 acres of wooded parkland and situated between Doncaster and Bawtry, near Robin Hood Airport. We provide the perfect setting for weddings, banquets, meetings and conferences. Our AA Rosette restaurant offers the finest cuisine and extensive wine list.

Details
David Rowley
01302 868696
Great North Road Nr
Rossington
Doncaster
DN11 0HW
South Yorkshire
F: **01302 865130**
E: **reception@mountpleasant.co.uk**
W: **www.mountpleasant.co.uk**

Hotels & restaurants

Mercure St Pauls

This luxury 4-star hotel offers 163 en suite rooms in the heart of Sheffield.

Details
Luisa Esposito
0114 2782000
119 Norfolk Street
Sheffield
S1 2JE
South Yorkshire
E: **luisa.esposito@accor.com**

Hotels & restaurants

Throapham House Bed & Breakfast

Five star, family run, luxury en-suite accommodation in Grade II Georgian property set in a rural location. Varied breakfast menu, free Wi-Fi, off road parking, within easy reach of M1/M18/A1/A57.

Details
Ann Holland
01909 562208
Throapham House Ltd
Olcotes Road, Throapham
Sheffield S25 2QS
South Yorkshire
E: **enquiries@throapham-house.co.uk**
W: **www.throapham-house.co.uk**

Outside caterers

PJ Taste

Showcasing local and regional producers we prepare fresh and exciting food every day. Enjoy our hospitality at our retail outlets or delivered to the location of your choice.

Details
Peter Moulam
0114 275 5971
249 Glossop Road
Sheffield S10 2GZ
South Yorkshire
E: **ask@pjtaste.co.uk**
W: **www.pjtaste.co.uk**

The Rutland Hotel

A truly unique hotel experience, The Rutland offers modern bedrooms with stunning design features, a warm and relaxed atmosphere, fresh local food, and an exceptional level of service that sets it apart from other hotels.

Details
Craig Dowie
0114 2664411
452 Glossop Road
Sheffield S10 2PY
South Yorkshire
F: **0114 2670348**
E: **reservations@rutlandhotel-sheffield.com**
W: **www.rutlandhotel-sheffield.com**

Wortley Arms

Customers can enjoy themselves in our warm welcoming environment, whilst enjoying a locally brewed ale or some excellent fresh food like our famous Wortley Pie, in front of our wood fire.

Details
Andy Gabittas
0114 2888749
Halifax Road, Wortley,
Sheffield, South Yorkshire
S35 7DB
E: **enquiries2008@wortley-arms.co.uk**
W: **www.wortley-arms.co.uk**

Did you know?

The food and drink sector's annual contribution to the regional economy is worth £8 billion *(ONS 2008)*

Deli & independent grocers

Brittain's Raspberry Vodka

Brittain's Raspberry Vodka, created using a blend of the finest fresh Yorkshire raspberries, is expertly infused with premium vodka (37.5%) to produce a soft delicious drink with a fruity aroma and exceptional flavour making it a true delight to drink. Visit the website for full product information and inspiring cocktail recipes.

Details

John Raper
01302 855010
Treetops Park Drive
Sprotbrough
Doncaster
DN5 7LN
South Yorkshire
E: **john@brittainsraspberryvodka.com**
W: **www.brittainsraspberryvodka.com**

Deli & independent grocers

Urban Deli

Urban Deli is situated just a few minutes walk from the cathedral. In addition to the wide selection of food available from the deli we also provide a relaxed eating experience with classic British dishes featuring heavily on the menu – from the locally sourced full English breakfast to a light lunch. Urban Deli also has an extensive external catering service produced fresh to order.

Details

Phil Mottram
0114-2763218
Unit 1a Campo Lane
Sheffield
S1 2EG
South Yorkshire
F: **0114 276 3218**
E: **phil.mottram@urbandeli.co.uk**
W: **www.urbandeli.co.uk**

Deli & independent grocers

Wilkinson Butchers Ltd

A traditional third generation family butcher, selling locally farmed beef, pork and lamb. Award winning sausages and bacon a speciality. Shops in Doncaster and Bawtry or order online.

Details

Trevor Wilkinson
01302 365834
25 Market Hall
Doncaster
DN1 1NG
South Yorkshire
E: **enquiries@wilkinson-butchers.com**
W: **www.wilkinson-butchers.co.uk**

Did you know?

The Bingley Arms at Bardsey, near Leeds, is the oldest pub in Britain: it's been around since AD905 and used to be called The Priests Inn as it was a popular spot for travelling monks to rest.

Billy's Hill Farm Shop

We're a friendly, family-run farm shop selling only the very best of locally sourced produce with our on-site reared, slowly matured beef and exquisite home baked pies and cakes being our speciality!

Details

Oliver Wright
01226 754744
Hemingfield Road
Hemingfield
Barnsley
S73 0PZ
South Yorkshire
F: **01226 754744**
E: **oewright@hotmail.co.uk**
W: **www.billyshillfarmshop.co.uk**

Farm shops

Cannon Hall Farm Shop

Cannon Hall Farm Shop offers the best in Yorkshire produce alongside the finest food from around the world. We bake a spectacular selection of homemade pies and freshly baked bread daily. We market food produced with principles and integrity delivering quality meat from the farm on which it was produced.

Details

Robert Nicholson
01226 790427
Cannon Hall Farm
Bark House Lane
Cawthorne
Barnsley
S75 4AT
South Yorkshire
E: **cannonhallfarm@btconnect.com**
W: **www.cannonhallfarm.co.uk**

Farm shops

Marr Grange Farm Shop

We are a family-run business specialising in home dry cured bacon and gammon. We produce and sell our own pork and local beef, lamb and chicken. We also have a wide range of homemade pies and cakes. Open: Thursday and Friday 9.30am-6pm, Saturday 9.30am-5pm.

Details

Ian Randall
01302 783930
Marr Farm
Doncaster
DN5 7AS
South Yorkshire
W: **www.marrgrangefarmshop.co.uk**

McCallums Bank End Farm Shop

McCallums is an ideal place to shop for specialist and everyday produce. Ranging from local beef, pork and lamb to fruit from our farm, alongside 70 other local suppliers – we're well worth a visit!

Details

David McCallum
01302 770224
Bank End
Bankend Road
Finningley
Doncaster
DN9 3NT
South Yorkshire
F: **01302 770224**
E: **davidmccallum@btconnect.com**
W: **www.mccallumsfarm.co.uk**

Rob Royd Farm Shop

Rob Royd Farm Shop produces and sells only the finest quality produce from its own farm and other local suppliers. With an in-house butchery, bakery, delicatessen and home and locally grown vegetables it really is fine foods fresh from the farm.

Details

Robert White
01226 248662
Genn Lane
Worsborough
Barnsley
S70 6NP
South Yorkshire
E: **info@robroydfarmshop.co.uk**

Whirlow Hall Farm Trust

High welfare meat and eggs exclusively from our farm, local free range chicken, wide range of homegrown vegetables and PYO fruit in summer. Snack servery open weekends and school holidays.

Details

Cath Morley
0114 235 2678
Whirlow Lane, Sheffield
S11 9QF South Yorkshire
F: **0114 262 1015**
E: **cathm@whirlowhallfarm.org**
W: **www.whirlowhallfarm.co.uk**

Wortley Farm Shop Ltd

Situated in the heart of the picturesque village of Wortley, committed to selling local, traditionally reared meat, their own sausages, burgers and pies, and top quality local produce.

Details

Andrea O'Connell
0114 288 2232
Park Avenue
Wortley
Sheffield S35 7DB
South Yorkshire
W: **www.wortleyfarmshop.co.uk**

DISTRIBUTORS

Fenwick Haulage

Fenwick Haulage provides temperature controlled solutions from 1kg to 9500kgs food, non food, pharmaceuticals with temperature printouts and satellite tracking. Fenwicks Foodservice provides a one-stop shop for the catering industry.

Details

Tommy McGregor-Smith
01302 728496
Church Lane, Adwick Le Street
Doncaster DN6 7AY
South Yorkshire
E: **fenwick.haulage@virgin.net**
W: **www.fenwickhaulage.co.uk**

West Yorkshire

West Yorkshire has plenty to offer with thriving centres like Leeds, Bradford and Wakefield attracting people for many reasons: magnificent museums, galleries, theatres, restaurants and bars. This is an area of dramatic landscapes too. Walk across the same Pennine moors that inspired the Brontë sisters or amble through the cobbled streets of villages that grew up during the industrial revolution.

For fantastic dining at the heart of West Yorkshire, Leeds is a delight for the gourmet with an eclectic mix of eateries all presenting a fine array of quality and choice.

Delve into Bradford's historical past and up-and-coming arts scene and enjoy good food and great curries – Bradford has a reputation as the region's curry capital.

Outside Bradford the food and drink trail goes on. You may stumble across vineyards and breweries and West Yorkshire is even famed for its rhubarb triangle.

This area is vibrant, contemporary and exciting, in so many ways that will surprise you.

The Old Post Office, Leeds

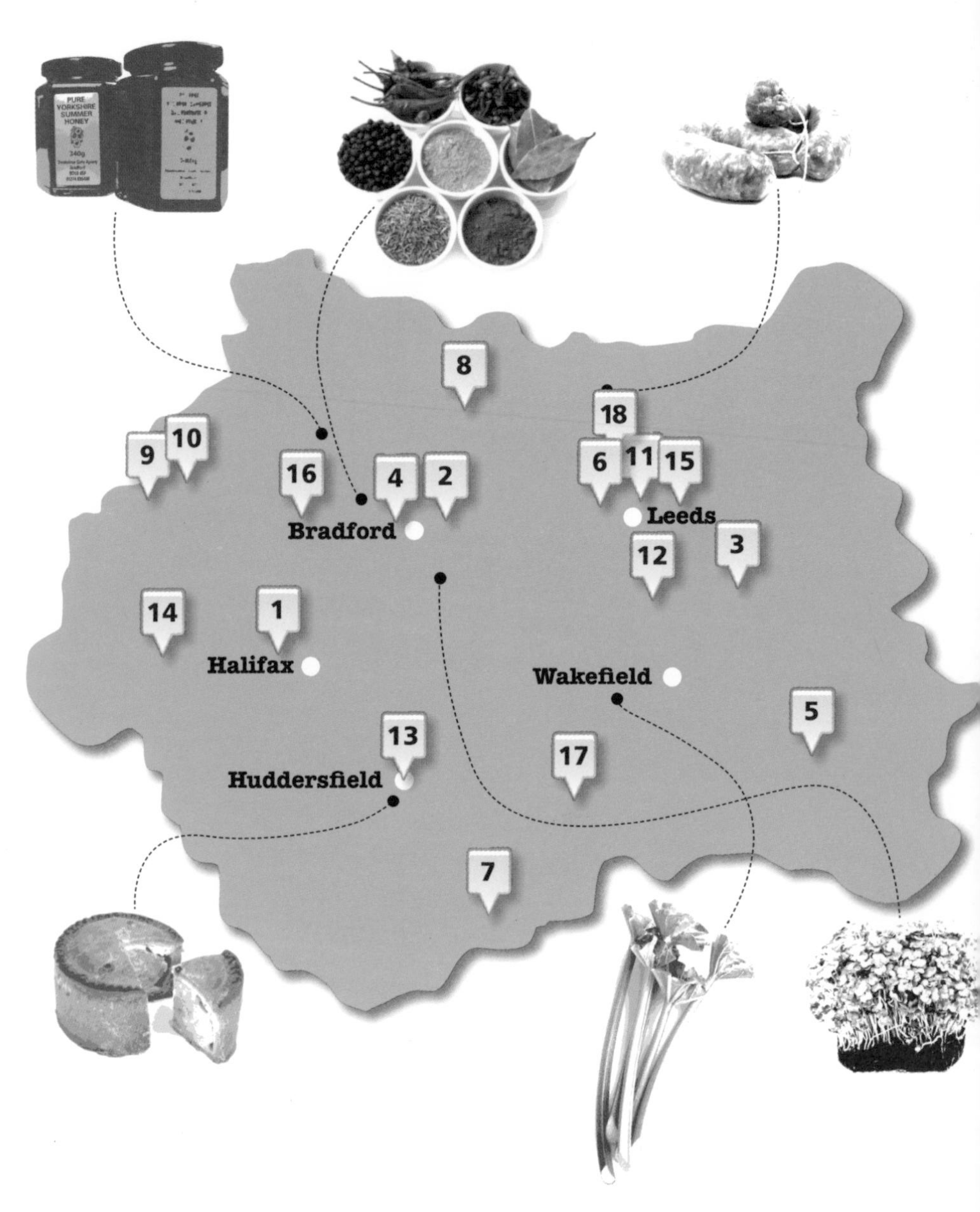
PURE YORKSHIRE SUMMER HONEY
340g
8
18
9
10
16
4
2
6
11
15
Bradford
Leeds
3
12
14
1
Halifax
Wakefield
5
13
17
Huddersfield
7

Food Highlights

Bakers & Confectioners

Bagel Nash Ltd

Bagel Nash is one of the fastest growing dedicated bagel businesses in Europe. Our bakery produces gourmet bagels, muffins and brownies, made to original recipes using the finest natural ingredients.

Details

Karen Mizrahi
0113 2930393
Buslingthorpe Green
Meanwood, Leeds
LS7 2HG
West Yorkshire
E: **sales@bagelnash.com**
W: **www.bagelnash.com**

Did you know?

More than 90% of the world's forced rhubarb was once produced in Yorkshire - and the Yorkshire Rhubarb Triangle, between Leeds, Bradford and Wakefield, is still going strong.

Bakers & Confectioners

Bloc Chocolate

Dark chocolate specialists with a flair for shape and form. Single origin and plantation chocolate available. Watch the chocolatiers at work in this little gem of a shop.

Details

Julia Cameron
01422 330458
65 The Piece Hall
Halifax
HX6 4EF
West Yorkshire
E: **julia@bloc-chocolate.co.uk**

Bakers & Confectioners

Brazilian Flavours Ltd

Discover Isabel's home-baking mixes – with inspiring natural flavours and wonderful textures giving you the best thin-crust pizza you'll ever taste and mouth-watering bite-size cheesebreads. Naturally gluten and wheat free, no artificial preservatives, no artificial flavours, no artificial colours, no hydrogenated fats, suitable for vegetarians and low in salt.

Details

Isabel Gordon
0871 2313399
Commerce Court
Challenge Way,
Cutler Heights Lane
Bradford
BD4 8NW
West Yorkshire
E: **bel@brazilianflavours.net**
W: **www.brazilianflavours.net**

The Cupcake Shoppe Ltd

The Cupcake Shoppe is the first cupcake bakery in Yorkshire specialising in bespoke cupcakes for all occasions. Our flavours range from cookies 'n' crème to peanut butter. Trade accounts welcome.

Details

Crystal Ourique
07796 273320
19a East Parade
Leeds
LS1 2BH West Yorkshire
E: **crystal@thecupcakeshoppe.co.uk**
W: **www.thecupcakeshoppe.co.uk**

Grandma Wilds Biscuits

Grandma Wilds award winning biscuits baked on trays, ensuring wholesome, crunchy biscuits baked without compromise in the traditional way.

Details

John Bateman
01535 650500
The Bakery, Millenium Business Park, Station Road, Steeton
Keighley BD20 6RB
West Yorkshire
F: **01535 650509**
W: **www.grandma-wilds.co.uk**

Bakers & Confectioners

Johnson's Toffees

Johnson's Toffees is a family run business, with over 70 years experience manufacturing quality confectionery. Only the finest ingredients are used to produce creamy caramel toffees and a vast selection of fudges and truffles. As we manufacture all of our own products we can guarantee a consistent high standard, using traditional methods.

Details

Tony Johnson
01977 515961
Carrwood Road
Glasshoughton
Castleford
WF10 4SB
West Yorkshire

Bakers & Confectioners

Joseph Dobsons and Sons

The home of the famous Yorkshire Mixture, Joseph Dobson's is a fascinating story of a family owned business which, from humble Victorian origins, has prospered to become one of the largest privately owned confectionery manufacturers in Yorkshire.

Details

Stephen Walshaw
01422 372165
26 Northgate
Elland
HX5 0RU
West Yorkshire
E: **stephen@dobsons.co.uk**

Just Desserts

Award winning bakers and patissiers, established for nearly 25 years, supplying the food service industry with a range of handmade desserts and quiches.

Details

James O'Dwyer
01274 590698
Unit 1, Station Road
Shipley BD18 2JL
West Yorkshire
F: **01274 590698**
E: **just-desserts@dsl.pipex.com**
W: **www.just-desserts.co.uk**

Bakers & Confectioners

Lauden Chocolate

LAUDEN CHOCOLATE

We produce handmade chocolates using the finest ingredients. They are visually beautiful and taste fantastic, as our 2009 bronze award from the Academy of Chocolate indicates. We sell direct to consumers and to trade loose boxed chocolates.

Details

Sun Trigg
0113 2440289
63 Brussels Street
Leeds LS9 8AB
West Yorkshire
E: **sun.trigg@lauden.co.uk**
W: **www.lauden.co.uk**

Bakers & Confectioners

Proper Maid

Award winning Huddersfield company, famous for creating cakes with a twist. An innovative range including; beetroot & chocolate and dandelion & burdock. Serving an emerging gap for unique homemade cakes.

Details

Allison Whitmarsh
01484 429285
43 Carr Street
Marsh, Huddersfield
HD3 4AU
West Yorkshire
E: **allison@propermaid.co.uk**

Thomas's Bakery

A wholesale, craft family bakery specialising in producing and delivering teacakes, bread and confectionery. Have recently launched "Lottie Shaws Seriously Good Yorkshire Parkin" which is now available around the region.

Details

Charlotte Shaw
01422 372335
84 Southgate
Elland HX5 0EP
West Yorkshire
F: **01422 377798**
E: **info@yorkshirebakery.co.uk**
W: **www.yorkshirebakery.co.uk**

Beverages (alcoholic & non)

Little Valley Brewery

Organic Beers produced with love and passion. Award winning organic real ales brewed by our Master Brewer in the beautiful surroundings of Pennine Yorkshire. Little Valley's beers are approved by the Soil Association and the Vegan Society. The brewery is also licensed by the Fairtrade Foundation for the 'Ginger Pale Ale'. Available in bottle, cask and polypin.

Details

Sue Cooper
01422 883888
Turkey Lodge
New Road, Cragg Vale
Hebden Bridge
HX7 5TT
West Yorkshire
F: **01422 883222**
E:**info@littlevalleybrewery.co.uk**
W: **www.littlevalleybrewery.**

everages (alcoholic & non)

The Punch Brew Company

Yorkshire Punch is a non alcoholic drink made from 14 different herbs carefully chosen to relax and cheer as nature intended. Superb new and improved fruity taste, can be served hot to relax or cold to refresh.

Details
Greg Fildes
01744 600981
49 Queensway
Mossbank St. Helens
WA11 7BY
(Head Office)
E: **enquiries@punchbrew.com**
W: **www.punchbrew.com**

airy & Eggs

Charlotte's Jersey Ice Cream Ltd

Our herd of Jersey cows produces the milk and double cream used in our luxury artisan dairy ice cream, with natural ingredients and comes in 24 flavours.

Details
Audrey Wraithmell
01924 494491
The Meadows
Lane Top Farm, Whitley
Dewsbury WF12 0NQ
West Yorkshire
F: **01924 498092**
E: **info@charlottesjerseyicecream.co.uk**

Dairy & Eggs

Cryer & Stott

At Cryer & Stott cheesemongers our aim is simple, to be the premier merchant of Yorkshire cheese and produce. Cryer & Stott own three deli shops. Named in the top 15 cheese merchants by 'The Independent' newspaper. Consultant to Channel 4 television. Named 'Business of the Year' by 'The Regional Food Group for Yorkshire and Humber'. Producer of Ruby Gold the worlds' only rhubarb cheese, which won a gold medal at the Nantwich Cheese Awards.

Details
Richard Holmes
01977 510638
5 Weir View
Castleford
WF10 2SF
West Yorkshire
E: **info@cryerandstott.co.uk**
W: **www.cryerandstott.co.uk**

Dairy & Eggs

Just Jenny's Farmhouse Ice Cream

Just Jenny's are passionate about making ice cream. Jenny makes it on the family farm using milk and cream from her own lovely cows. All ingredients are natural, fresh and locally sourced.

Details
Jenny Clarkson
01422 823268
Hazel Slack Farm
Barkisland
Halifax HX4 0DU
West Yorkshire
F: **01422 823268**
E: **jenny@justjennys.co.uk**

Did you know?

The Bingley Arms at Bardsey, near Leeds, is the oldest pub in Britain: it's been around since AD905 and used to be called The Priests Inn as it was a popular spot for travelling monks to rest.

Fresh Ingredients

D. Westwood & Son

A large variety of crops are grown such as rhubarb, cauliflower, broccoli and a variety of cabbages. The specialist rhubarb crop is grown in the heart of the famous Yorkshire Rhubarb Triangle. All the products are supplied loose or pre-packed as required by the customer. Contact Westwood's for further information.

Details

David Westwood
01924 822314
Thorpe Lane Farm
Thorpe, Wakefield
WF3 3BZ
West Yorkshire
F: **01924 870668**
W: **www.dwsyorkshireboxes.co.uk**

Fresh Ingredients

E. Oldroyd & Sons Ltd

Producers and packers of high quality fruit, vegetables and rhubarb to supermarkets, packers, processors, wholesalers and retail outlets. This long established company has a high media profile and has received many awards, including Rick Stein Food Hero. Visits/talks (Jan-March), rhubarb by mail order. BRC, Field to Fork, Nature's Choice and Assured Produce accredited.

Details

Janet Oldroyd
0113 2822245
Hopefield Farm
The Shutts, Leadwell Lane
Rothwell
Leeds LS26 0ST
West Yorkshire
F: **0113 282 8775**
E: **janet@eoldroyd.co.uk**
W: **www.yorkshirerhubarb.co.uk**

Fresh Ingredients

Farnley Estates

Growing fruit, vegetables and crops on our own estate at Farnley Tyas.

Details

Paul Sykes
01484 667744
Farnley House, Manor Road
Farnley Tyas, Huddersfield
HD4 6UL West Yorkshire
F: **01484 662244**
E: **paulsykes@shawspetroleum.co.uk**
W: **www.farnleyestates.co.uk**

Troy Foods

Vegetable processor and dressed salads manufacturer. The business i based in Leeds.

Details

Sara Clayton
0113 2721433
1a George Man Way
Leeds LS10 1DR
West Yorkshire
F: **0113 383 8406**
E: **andrew@troyfoods.co.uk**
E: **sclayton@troyfoods.co.uk**

esh Ingredients

Green Field Produce

GREEN FIELD PRODUCE

Whole head and prepared produce growers and suppliers. Produce includes cabbage, cauliflower, broccoli, rhubarb, swede, potatoes, carrots and onions. Fully BRC accredited with full traceability and quality assurance.

Details

Carl Smales
0113 2827811
Ouzlewell Green
Lofthouse, Wakefield
WF3 3QW West Yorkshire
E: **admin@greenfieldproduce.co.uk**

Ingredient Suppliers

Gordon Rhodes & Son

Gordon Rhodes & Son is a Grade A, BRC Certified seasoning manufacturer, producing bespoke flavours for the meat, fish and bakery industries. The product portfolio contains over 3000 recipes – sausage and burger seasonings, stuffing, black pudding, sauce and gravy mixes, pie and pasty seasonings, curing compounds, glazes and coaters.

Details

Jayne Horrocks
01274 758000
Dalesman House
Chaseway
Bradford
BD5 8HW
West Yorkshire
F: **01274 758009**
E: **taste@dalesman.co.uk**

Ingredient Suppliers

Ulrick & Short

Ulrick&Short 

Ulrick & Short supply clean label functional food ingredients, which are completely free from chemical, enzymic or genetic modification. We specialise in ingredients for bakery, processed meats, sauces and coatings.

Details

Andrew Ulrick
01977 620011
Walton Wood Farm
Thorpe Audlin
Pontefract
WF8 3HQ
West Yorkshire
F: **01977 620022**
W: **www.ulrickandshort.com**

Meat, poultry & game (fresh & smoked)

Andrews Butchers Ltd

At Andrew's Butchers we pride ourselves on being a small family owned business where we source all our products locally. All our staff can give expert advice on the products we sell.

Details
Andrew Veale
01937 582063
8 North Street
Wetherby
LS22 6NN
West Yorkshire
E: **nichola.veale@ntlworld.com**

Lishman's of Ilkley

High quality traditional butchers producing home cured hams, bacon, championship sausage and black puddings, using livestock born and bred in Yorkshire.

Details
David Lishman
01943 603809
23-27 Leeds Road
Ilkley LS29 8DP
West Yorkshire
F: **01943 603809**
E: **david@lishmansofilkley.co.uk**

Meat, poultry & game (fresh & smoked)

Far Isle Farm

Welcome to Far Isle Farm – a family run business. Naturally reared meats are our speciality. With over 30 years experience on the farm and in the farm shop, we can offer a full range of handmade sausages, poultry, beef, lamb, dry cured bacon and game. Mail order service available.

Details
Chris Argent
01422 244859
259 Shay Lane
Holmfield
Halifax
HX2 9AG
West Yorkshire
F: **01422 246343**
W: **www.farislefarm.co.uk**

Meat, poultry & game (fresh & smoked)

Wilsons of Crossgates

Wilsons, voted "England's Best Butchers 2005 – 2006", supply the finest locally reared beef, lamb and free range pork from their Crossgates shop along with award winning black pudding, sausages and pies.

Details
John/Andrew Green
0113 2645448
38 Austhorpe Road
Crossgates, Leeds LS15 8DX
West Yorkshire
F: **0113 2930516**
E: **john@wilsonsbutchers.co.uk**
W: **www.wilsonsbutchers.co.uk**

Pies

The Crusty Pie Company

Traditional and speciality pies, pasties and sausage rolls, sold with our own range of delicious chutney.

Details
Richard Edhouse
01274 673664
Lion Gate House Bakery
Stanage Lane, Shelf
Halifax
HX3 7PR
West Yorkshire
E: **richard@crustypie.co.uk**

ndrew Jones ies) Ltd

/e produce a range of quality ies using locally sourced gredients, delivering across e North of England with aked or unbaked pies. We ere the proud winners of the eliciouslyorkshire Supreme roduct of the Year 2008-09 ith our Figit Pie.

etails

ndrew Jones
1484 548137
nits 2,3 & 4 Queens Mill
dustrial Estate
ueens Mill Lane
uddersfield
D1 1RR
/est Yorkshire
: **01484 548138**
: **info@piesnpasties.co.uk**
: **www.piesnpasties.co.uk**

Pies

The Denby Dale Pie Company

Based in Denby Dale where the world's largest pie was baked, we provide high quality frozen meat pies. Using traditional methods, handmade from preparation to finishing, including the best quality ingredients such as chuck steak.

Details

Janet Purcell
01484 862585
Unit 12, Denby Dale Business Park
Wakefield Road
Denby Dale
Huddersfield
HD8 8QH
West Yorkshire
E: **janet@thedenbydalepiecoltd.fsnet.co.uk**
W: **www.denbydalepiecompany.co.uk**

Pies

John Lord & Sons (Take & Bake)

Our mission is to restore the humble pork pie to its rightful place in the hearts and minds of ordinary folk. Traditional pork pies of all shapes and sizes, plus alternative fillings and bespoke pies made to order. New retail outlet at Huddersfield Open Market – Byram Street, Huddersfield, HD1 1RX, open Mondays, Tuesdays, Thursdays & Saturdays.

Details

John Lord
0845 6860331
6 Thorn Avenue
Heaton
Bradford
BD9 6LS
West Yorkshire
E: **mail@jlordandson.co.uk**
W: **www.jlordandson.co.uk**

Prepared Food

AreOlives

- Traditional greek olives in a variety of delicious marinades and olive oil
- Olives grown in Greece, made in Yorkshire
- Unique marinades fresh to order
- State of the art production unit near Wetherby, working to BRC standards
- Olives, olive oil, semi-dried tomatoes and delicious deli products

Details

Paul Jenner
01937 844600
Unit 4 Ash Way, Thorp Arch Estate
Wetherby
LS23 7FA
West Yorkshire
F: **01937 845600**
W: **www.areolives.com**

Prepared Food

Foodamentalists

Made using great local produce, our ready to heat and eat meals conform to our high ethical standards. With nothing nasty added they taste homemade and make being good easy.

Details

Stevan Taylor
07884 064130
9 Britannia Works
Skinner Lane, Pontefract
WF8 1NA
West Yorkshire
E: **info@foodamentalists.co.uk**
W: **www.foodamentalists.co.uk**

Did you know?

World-renowned British retailer Marks and Spencer started as a stall at Kirkgate Market, Leeds in 1884. The first stall is marked today with a green and gold commemorative clock.

Prepared Food

Mumtaz Ventures Ltd

The world famous Mumtaz is recognised around the world for fine food and excellent products, creating ranges of restaurant quality food in frozen, chilled and ambient formats, for customers to enjoy at home. Mumtaz uses authentic spices and ingredien to create unique products that are unparalleled for qualit and taste.

Details

Bill Kimberling
0870 77786786
Units 1-3 Orchard Business Pa
Scout Road, Mytholmroyd
Halifax
HX7 5HZ
West Yorkshire
E: **bill@mumtaz.com**
W: **www.mumtaz.com**

epared Food

Seabrook Crisps Ltd

ieabrook are the North's
best-loved crisps. They've
always been known for their
full flavour, crunch and purer
ngredients – like sunflower oil
and sea salt and now all 18
flavours are free from nasties
like MSG.

Details

Phil Devine
01274 546405

**Seabrook House
Duncombe Street, Ingleby
Road, Bradford BD8 9AJ
West Yorkshire**
T: **01274 542235**
W: **www.seabrookcrisps.com**

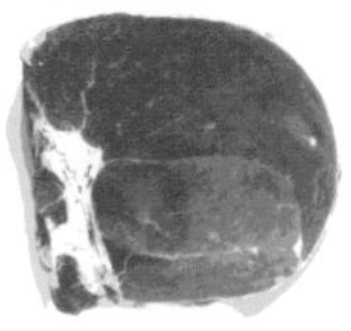

Did you know?

319,283

There are 319,283 heads of beef cattle in the county – nearly a quarter of the English total

Prepared Food

Tiffin Foods UK

Producer of convenience foods for the retail, public health, travel, forecourt, and education sectors. From biodegradable packaged sandwiches to hot serves. What differentiates us from others is the time, dedication and emphasis we place on our customers, food safety, brand marketing, market analysis, product development and the environment.

Details

John Varey
01274 494939

**Prospect Works
Allerton
Bradford
BD15 7AF
West Yorkshire**
F: **01274 494939**
W: **www.tiffin-foods.co.uk**

Preserves, honey, condiments & spices

Curry Cuisine Ltd

Indian authenticity with Yorkshire provenance – a range of premium award winning pickles and chutneys using local produce with a spicy twist! Spice mixes, onion bhaji mix and Indian salad dressings available in catering sizes as well as retail. Indian cookery lessons, cooperate team building and cookery demonstrations available.

Details

Paresh Tejura
0113 2189685

**3 Turnberry Drive
Tingley
Wakefield
WF3 1AQ
West Yorkshire**
E: **enquiries@currycuisine.co.uk**
W: **www.currycuisine.co.uk**

PRODUCERS

Preserves, honey, condiments & spices

Denholme Gate Apiary

We are a small producer of pure Yorkshire honey, specialising in spring blossom, summer flower, borage and heather honey, all harvested from the varied flora of the Yorkshire countryside.

Details

Liz Joyce

01274 835490

The Gatehouse, Brighouse Road, Denholme Gate, Bradford

BD13 4EP West Yorkshire

F: **01274 835490**

W: **www.denholmegatehoney.co.uk**

Shaws of Huddersfield Ltd

An independent family business manufacturing quality chutney, relish, salsa and sauces to both retail and catering customers. There are over 60 to choose from. Which is your favourite?

Details

Daniel Shaw

01484 539999

Shaw Park Office Centre

Silver Street

Huddersfield

HD5 9AF

West Yorkshire

W: **www.shaws1889.com**

Preserves, honey, condiments & spices

Wharfe Valley Farms

Wharfe Valley Extra Virgin Cold Pressed Rapeseed Oil is grown, pressed and bottled by the Kilby's. With half the saturated fat of olive oil and 10 times more Omega 3, its health benefits are proving to be a Great British alternative.
Try our exciting new additions – Oak Smoked & Red Chilli.
All available in retail and catering sizes.

Details

Geoff Kilby

01937 572084

Lilac Farm

Jewitt Lane

Collingham

LS22 5BA

West Yorkshire

W: **www.wharfevalleyfarms.co.uk**

HOSPITALITY

Café & tearoom

Cafe 1842 – Armitage's Pennine Garden Centre

Café 1842

With beautiful views of the Pennine countryside, Café 1842 at Armitage's Pennine Garden Centre offers delicious homemade dishes, daily specials, light meals and tempting cakes and pastries. Proud of our locality and the good food in Yorkshire, our menu boasts local ingredients including bacon and sausage served with our hearty breakfasts, available Mon to Sat from 9.30-11am and Sun from 10.30am to 12pm.

Details

Sue Smith

01484 607248

Armitage's Pennine Garden Centre, Huddersfield Road, Shelley

HD8 8LF West Yorkshire

E: **cafe1842@armitages.com**

W: **www.armitages.com**

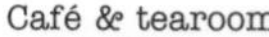

fé & tearoom

The Cooking School at Dean Clough Ltd

A unique setting in which to learn new cooking skills. Catering for the leisure customer, corporate market and offers professional development courses for educationalists and health professionals. What makes it truly special is that all profits are gifted to the Focus on Food Campaign, providing free cooking lessons to children UK wide.

Details

Emma Pira
01422 383192
D Mill
Dean Clough
Halifax
HX6 5AX
West Yorkshire
E: **emma@thecookingschool.co.uk**
W: **www.thecookingschool.co.uk**
W: **www.focusonfood.org**

Café & tearoom

Cranberries

cranberries

Cranberries deli is filled with lots of interesting and delicious Yorkshire goodies. In our continental style shop, we serve breakfast, snacks, cakes and award winning coffee. We also have an exciting range of pottery, gifts, and cards. Outdoor catering and hampers to suit all budgets and occasions. Open 7 days.

Details

Jeremey & Shelley Carlsen
0113 2300293
471 Otley Road
Adel, Leeds
LS16 7NR
West Yorkshire
E: **info@cranberrieshampers.com**
W: **www.cranberrieshampers.com**

Café & tearoom

The Old Shop Café – Armitage's Birchencliffe Garden Centre

The Old Shop Cafe

Established in 1842 and proud of our locality and the good food here in Yorkshire, the Old Shop Café at Armitage's Birchencliffe Garden Centre offers delicious homemade dishes, daily specials and light meals plus tempting homemade cakes and pastries. Boasting regional ingredients including bacon and sausage, our hearty breakfasts are served Mon to Sat from 9.30-11am and on Sun from 10.30am to 12pm.

Details

Richard Kendrick
01484 536010
Armitage's Birchencliffe Garden Centre
75 Birchencliffe Hill Road
Huddersfield
HD3 3NJ
West Yorkshire
W: **www.armitages.com**
E: **oldshopcafe@armitages.com**

Café & tearoom

Pickles & Potter Deli Cafe

Pickles & Potter's two thriving deli cafés focus on using local Yorkshire suppliers – bringing us the best in fresh produce to enable our chefs and sandwich-makers to create award-winning sandwiches, fresh salads, soups, hot main courses and delicious cakes.

Details

Lorna Potter
0113 2427702
18-20 Queens Arcade
Leeds LS1 6LF
West Yorkshire
E: **info@picklesandpotter.co.uk**
W: **www.picklesandpotter.co.uk**

Café & tearoom

Whiteleys

Elegant cafe Whiteleys offers first class service with a wide range of hot meals, snacks, cold and hot drinks in a beautiful surrounding. Our five chefs create mouth watering homemade food fresh on the premises using the finest ingredients. Breakfast starts at 9am six days a week and 10am on a Sunday (served until 11.30).

Details

Alex Plumbridge
01924 495944
Leeds Road (A62)
Mirfield
WF4 0DQ
West Yorkshire
F: **01924 489600**
E: **info@whiteleys-gc.co.uk**

Café & tearoom

Yummy Yorkshire Ice Cream Company

Award winning luxurious ice cream made exclusively at Delph House Farm from fresh milk and cream of the Fresian Holstein herd. Over 50 recipes of traditional, seasonal and contemporary ice cream is produced using quality ingredients from locally sourced suppliers and served in the delightful ice cream parlour and coffee shop on the farm every day from 11am to 5pm. Existing and new customers are always welcome to attend promotional events throughout the year too.

Details

Jeremy Holmes
01226 762551
Delph House Farm
High Flatts, Denby
Huddersfield HD8 8XY
West Yorkshire
F: **01226 762888**
E: **sales@yorkshiremilk.co.uk**
W: **www.yorkshiremilk.co.uk**

fé & tearoom

Yorkshire Deli

'orkshire Deli is a café, shop and online store selling only produce nade in Yorkshire. Our café nenu is packed with ingredients ourced from deliciouslyorkshire nembers, many of whose products are also available to buy n our shop or online.

Details
'an Taylor
)1943 817387
27 The Grove Promenade
Ilkley
LS29 8AF
West Yorkshire
E: **mail@yorkshiredeli.co.uk**
W: **www.yorkshiredeli.co.uk**

Hotels & restaurants

Anthony's Restaurant Limited

Anthony's Restaurant is our flagship restaurant with a reputation for creative and innovative cuisine to the highest of standards, offering a true gastronomic experience without pretence, appealing to all food lovers.

Details
Anthony Flinn
0113 2455922
19 Boar Lane, Leeds LS1 6EA
West Yorkshire
E: **anthony@anthonysrestaurant.co.uk**
W: **www.anthonysrestaurant.co.uk**

Hotels & restaurants

Ashmount Country House

Stay in the former home of Dr. Amos Ingham, physician to Charlotte and Patrick Bronte. Built in 1870, the original Gothic interiors of the house are well preserved and most of the furnishings are Victorian. Fantastic views of the moors.

Details
Gill Capeling
01535 645726
Mytholmes Lane, Haworth
BD22 8EZ West Yorkshire
E: **enquiries@ashmounthaworth.co.uk**
E: **info@ashmounthaworth.co.uk**
W: **www.ashmounthaworth.co.uk**

otels & restaurants

42 The Calls

This refreshingly different, townhouse hotel, has a unique location, with the advantage of a peaceful setting overlooking the river Aire and being only a few minutes walk from the city centre. 42 The Calls was converted in 1991 from a cornmill and since opening, has won no fewer than 10 major awards or accolades.

Details
Belinda Dawson
0113 2440099
Leeds
LS2 7EW
E: **hotel@42thecalls.co.uk**

Apna Khana

As one of the leading Indian caterers in the UK we strive to provide our customers with the total satisfaction of a high quality and authentic Punjabi and Gujarati cuisine.

Details
Karan Kaushal
07904 460176
58 Banner Street
Off Leeds Road, Bradford
BD3 9RH, West Yorkshire
E: **info@apnakhana.co.uk**

The Black Olive Delicatessen

The Black Olive is a food lovers' paradise, providing beautifully presented produce with personal and friendly service. We pride ourselves on featuring many regionally sourced items.

Details
Mike Adams
01924 275984
11 Queen Street
Horbury, Wakefield
WF4 6LP West Yorkshire
E: **michaeladams007@btinternet.com**

Hotels & restaurants

Briar Court Hotel

A warm welcome and great location. We at Briar Court Hotel pride ourselves on 20 years of experience of looking after our guests, whether your stay is for business or simply for pleasure.

Details

Joanne Reynolds
01484 519902
Halifax Road, Birchencliffe
Huddersfield HD3 3NT
West Yorkshire
E: **info@briarcourthotel.co.uk**
W: **www.briarcourt.co.uk**

Did you know?

The Great Yorkshire Show goes back 171 years. It used to tour 30 towns before the innovative decision was made in 1950 to build a permanent showground in Harrogate.

Hotels & restaurants

The Butchers Arms

We aim to bring to the heart of Yorkshire, simple, yet stylish food in modern surroundings. Wherever possible we use regional, free range, freedom and sustainable foods that not only support local and regional suppliers, but offer our guests a truly regional flavour.

Details

Tim Bilton
01484 682361
38 Towngate
Hepworth
West Yorkshire
HD9 1TE
E: **thebutchersarmsathepworth@btconnect.com**
W: **www.thebutchersarmshepworth.co.uk**

Hotels & restaurants

Castle View Guest House

Luxury 5-star gold awarded guest house with panoramic vews over Pennine Yorkshire. Licensed, luxury spa hot tub, beauty facilities, Norwegian grill house.

Details

Andy Whiteley
01484 307460
148 Ashes Lane, Castle Hill
Huddersfield HD4 6TE
West Yorkshire
E: **info@castleviewyorkshire.co.uk**
W: **www.castleviewyorkshire.co.uk**

Cedar Court Hotel Bradford

Welcome to the Cedar Court Hotel Leeds/Bradford. Four star luxury at the foot of the Pennines. We're the perfect place to relax and put you in the right frame of mind for whatever you have in mind!

Details

Nick Testa
01274 406606
Mayo Avenue, Off Rooley Lane
Bradford BD5 8Hz
West Yorkshire
W: **www.cedarcourthotels.co.uk**

Cedar Court Hotel Huddersfield

his four-star hotel offers varm Yorkshire hospitality in a nodern, superbly located and onference-ready environment. here are 114 bedrooms, ncluding interconnecting ooms, four-poster suites and he deluxe Pennine Suite.

)etails
Ielen Stewart
)1422 375431
Ainley Top
Huddersfield HD3 3RH
West Yorkshire
W: **www.cedar-court-huddersfield.co.uk**

Cedar Court Hotel Wakefield

Cedar Court prides itself on sourcing local produce and food in our menus. Our current group initative has been our successful Yorkshire Breakfast menu in all of our hotels.

)etails
Michael Weaver
)1924 276310
Calder Grove
Denby Dale Road
Wakefield WF4 3QZ
West Yorkshire
W: **www.cedarcourthotels.co.uk**

Chevin Country Park Hotel & Spa

Chevin Country Park Hotel & Spa is a unique Yorkshire venue in a stunning woodland setting. Offering a high standard of accommodation in either hotel rooms or lodge rooms. The superb AA rosette Lakeside restaurant satisfies the most discerning of tastebuds. Stunning conference and wedding facilities also available.

Details
Enda Rylands
01943 467818
Yorkgate
Otley LS21 3NU
West Yorkshire
E: **chevin@crerarhotels.com**
W: **www.crerarhotels.co.uk**

Croft Mill

Stunning self catering apartments for the discerning guest located in the heart of the popular town of Hebden Bridge. Open all year for long or short breaks.

Details
Josephine Anderson
01422 846836
Croft Mill Yard, Hebden Bridge HX7 8AB
West Yorkshire
E: **josephine@croftmill.com**
W: **www.croftmill.com**

Did you know?

There are 1,139,348 lambs in Yorkshire – over a seventh of the English total

Cucina Restaurants Limited

We provide specialist fresh food to secondary schools throughout England focusing on preparing a wide range of hot and cold food on each site daily via award winning chefs.

Details

Steve Quinn
0845 389 1320
Poplar Farm
George Lane
Notton
WF4 2NQ
West Yorkshire

Hotels & restaurants

Digby Trout Restaurant

FILM NATIONAL MEDIA TELEVISION RADIO MUSEUM WEB PHOTOGRAPHY

Visitors to the Museum's café can purchase Yorkshire sourced products including crisps, Pennine spring water, and tea, whilst corporate clients can enjoy first-class event catering, with the benefit of increasing the sales and consumption of Yorkshire produce and significantly reducing the carbon footprint generated by their events.

Details

Anthony Hegney
01625 660160
National Media Museum
Bradford, BD1 1NQ
West Yorkshire
E: **nmem.digbytrout@nationalmediamuseum.org.uk**
W: **www.digbytrout.com**

Hotels & restaurants

Fennel Restaurant

Fennel café and restaurant offers dishes and wines celebrating the best of local produce, with plenty to please the traditional diner, whilst tempting the culinary explorer to try something new. Fennel proudly supports Yorkshire farmers and fishermen and ensures most ingredients are seasonal and sourced from within twenty miles.

Details

Lionel Strub
01937 586541
Victoria Court
Victoria Street
Wetherby
LS22 6YP
West Yorkshire
W: **www.justfennel.co.uk**

Field House B&B

Offering guests a warm and friendly welcome, this Grade II listed Yorkshire B&B near Halifax/Shibden Hall is an exquisite Grade II listed building full of charm and character, and beautifully appointed.

Details

Pat Horrocks-Taylor
01422 355457
Stalks Lane, Stump Cross
Halifax HX3 6XW
West Yorkshire
E: **stayatfieldhouse@yahoo.co.uk**
W: **www.fieldhouse-bb.co.uk**

The Gallery at Flannels

An incredible loft style room located on the 3rd floor of Flannels designer clothing store, in Leeds city centre. High quality, competitive pricing and a touch of Anthony's creativity can be found on the menu.

Details

Anthony Flinn (SNR)
0113 2428732
68 Vicar Lane
Leeds
LS1 7JH
West Yorkshire
E: **flannels@anthonysrestaurant.co.uk**

Hotels & restaurants

Great Victoria (Tomahawk Group)

GREAT VICTORIA TOMAHAWK®

The Great Victoria is housed in a landmark Victorian building in the centre of Bradford. Now sympathetically restored to its former glory and incorporating contemporary touches, the hotel includes the best bedrooms and penthouses in Bradford. The menu served in the impressive oak panelled restaurant features excellent fresh Yorkshire produce.

Details

Simon Grybas
01274 728706
Bridge Street
Bradford
BD1 1JX
West Yorkshire
E: **reservations@victoriabradford.co.uk**
W: **www.tomahawkhotels.co.uk**

Hotels & restaurants

Holme House

Holme House is a 5 star, gold rated bed & breakfast situated in the heart of Hebden Bridge.

Details

Sarah Eggleston
01422 847588
New Road
Hebden Bridge
HX7 8AD
West Yorkshire
E: **mail@holmehousehebdenbridge.co.uk**

Did you know?

Yorkshire Swine pigs are the most documented breed in the USA and Canada, found in almost every state. It's thought the first Yorkshires were taken to Ohio in

1830

Hotels & restaurants

The Huddersfield Central Lodge

When staying at the Lodge our full Yorkshire breakfast is not to be missed, whether in town for business or pleasure there's always time for a Yorkshire family cooked breakfast!

Details
Liz Wood
01484 515551
11-15 Beast Market
Huddersfield HD1 1QF
West Yorkshire
F: **01484 432349**
E: **joe@centrallodge.com**
W: **www.centrallodge.com**

Hotels & restaurants

Malmaison

The bar and brasserie are the heart and soul of the hotel. We work closely with local producers and suppliers to offer our home grown and local menu – all dishes include fresh, organic ingredients.

Details
Zara Goodwin
0113 3981000
1 Swinegate
Leeds
LS1 4AG
West Yorkshire
F: **0113 398 1002**
E: **leeds@malmaison.com**
W: **www.malmaison.com**

Hotels & restaurants

Manor Guest House

Lovingly restored, this 18th century Manor House is enhanced by many original features. Ideally situated for exploring the rugged Pennine Moorland of Bronte country, the Yorkshire Dales and beyond.

Details
Michelle Cotter
01535 274374
The Manor, Sutton Drive
Cullingworth Bradford
BD13 5BQ
West Yorkshire
E: **info@cullingworthmanor.co.uk**

Ivy Guest House

Close to Bradford City centre, this Grade II listed building is set among trees in a traditional cobbled street recalling Bradford's prosperous industrial heritage.

Details
Nick Baggio
01274 727060
3 Melbourne Place
Bradford
BD5 0HZ
West Yorkshire
E: **nickbaggio@aol.com**

Mama Mia's Cafe Bar

Details
01422 351209
Chew Magna Ltd
29 Horton Street
Halifax HX1 1QE
West Yorkshire
E: **andrewcmooney@tiscali.co.uk**

Milford Hotel

Whilst staying at the Milford Hotel, Leeds, enjoy a choice of dishes in our award winning Watermill Restaurant, which serves fresh, local produce from the Leeds and Yorkshire area, and features a working waterwheel.

Details
Shaun Sleath
01977 681800
Great North Rd
Peckfield
Leeds
LS25 5LQ
West Yorkshire
E: **enquiries@mlh.co.uk**

Hotels & restaurants

The Met Hotel

Located inside the Grade II listed grandeur of The Met, Leeds. Tempus Bar and Restaurant has a modern, contemporary feel, which prides itself on warm and friendly service. Head Chef Stephen Miller is a keen advocate of using locally sourced produce in his fresh seasonal menus.

Details

Chris Carr
0113 2450841
King Street
Leeds
LS1 2HQ
West Yorkshire
E: **chris.carr@principal-hayley.com**
W: **www.principal-hayley.com**

Hotels & restaurants

The Old Registry Ltd

A luxurious resting place in the heart of Bronte Country. Dedicated to the deliciouslyorkshire brand, our breakfast suppliers include Arthur Haigh, Bleikers, Farmhouse Preserves and we work closely with Lishman's of Ilkley who produce our bacon and make our sausages by request, without any preservatives, stabilisers, colourants etc.

Details

Paul Widdowson
01535 646503
2-4 Main Street, Haworth,
Nr Keighley BD22 8DA
West Yorkshire
F: **01535 646503**
W: **www.theoldregistryhaworth.co.uk**

Hotels & restaurants

Oulton Hall – Calverley Grill & Claret Jug

Oulton Hall's Claret Jug is a high-quality restaurant serving a number of delicious gastro-pub style dishes using the finest, local, fresh food. The newly refurbished Calverley Grill offers fine dining at its best.

Details

Louise Wright
0113 2821000
Rothwell Lane
Oulton, Leeds LS26 8HN
West Yorkshire
F: **0113 2828066**
W: **www.devere-hotels.com**

Radisson SAS

Radisson SAS Hotel Leeds with convenient facilities and extensive conferencing and meeting venues, is the ideal destination for business or leisure travellers alike.

Details

Jonathan Huglin
0113 2366007
No.1 The Light, The Headrow
Leeds LS1 8TL
West Yorkshire
F: **0113 2366100**
E: **jonathan.huglin@radissonsas.com**

Hotels & restaurants

Rombalds Hotel & Restaurant

Small town house style hotel situated in Ilkley on the edge of the Ilkley Moor yet only 600 yards from the town centre. AA rosetted restaurant offering traditional Yorkshire and British cuisine using locally sourced ingredients where possible.

Details

Colin R Clarkson
01943 603201
West View, Wells Road
Ilkley LS29 9JG
West Yorkshire
E: **reception@rombalds.demon.co.uk**
W: **www.rombalds.co.uk**

Rosebud Cottage Guest House

Traditional Yorkshire stone guest house dating from 1752 in the centre of Haworth. We have five luxury ensuite rooms to choose from, serving a deliciouslyorkshire breakfast using locally sourced produce.

Details

Caroline Starkey
01535 640321
1 Belle Isle, Haworth
Keighley BD22 8QQ
West Yorkshire
E: **info@rosebudcottage.co.uk**

Hotels & restaurants

Royal Armouries (International) plc

An Unforgettable Corporate Occasion…
Enjoy a breath taking experience as accomplished actors bring history to life…
The Royal Armouries Museum is the perfect place to entertain your guests with our range of deliciously Yorkshire foods, fine wines and world class entertainment.
Contact Janna Woods on 0113 220 1990 or email janna.wood@rai-events.co.uk"

Details

Janna Woods
07770 525413
Armouries Drive
Hunslet
Leeds
LS10 1LT
West Yorkshire
E: **neil.mccarthy@rai-events.co.uk**

Hotels & restaurants

Thorpe Park Hotel & Spa

Contemporary surroundings teamed perfectly with a strong emphasis on quality, locally sourced ingredients. Choose the stylish restaurant, the stunning internal limestone courtyard or dine al fresco on the terrace. Ideal for family parties and celebrations.

Details

Gordon Jackson
0113 2641000
1150 Century Way, Thorpe Par
Leeds LS15 8ZB West Yorkshire
F: **0113 264 1010**
E: **therestaurant@shirehotels.com**

Did you know?

The Yorkshire and Humber food and drink sector is the most diverse in the country

Tower House Executive Guest House

A stunning Victorian home restored to its original elegance offering elegantly decorated bedrooms, sleek furniture and extensive hotel facilities. Registered with Visit Britain Quality in Tourism and awarded the highest standard possible 5 stars and a prestigious gold award. Breakfast sourced locally as part of the deliciouslyyorkshire breakfast scheme.

Details

Carol Slatter
01977 699988
21 Bondgate
Pontefract
WF8 2JP
West Yorkshire
E: **info@towerhouseguesthouse.com**
W: **www.towerhouseguesthouse.com**

Waterfront Lodge Hotel

The Waterfront Lodge Hotel is situated on the banks of the Calder & Hebble Navigation, West Yorkshire. We are committed to providing the freshest ingredients for our guests to enjoy as part of their breakfast, lunch and evening meal.

Details

Fiona Walker
01484 715566
Huddersfield Road
Brighouse HD6 1JZ
West Yorkshire
F: **01484 715588**
E: **info@waterfrontlodge.co.uk**
W: **www.waterfrontlodge.co.uk**

Did you know?

There are 84 breweries in the historic county of Yorkshire, the oldest of which is Samuel Smith's Old Brewery at Tadcaster, founded in 1758.

Weavers Ltd

This restaurant with rooms has used the very best northern produce, since opening in 1978. Allotment gardeners, an accredited butcher, a local apiary, our own hens, cheesemakers, smokeries and dairies all play a part in putting AA rosette food on the plate.

Details

Colin Rushorth
01535 643822
13/17 West Lane
Haworth
BD22 8DU
West Yorkshire
E: **weaversltd@btconnect.com**
W: **www.weaversmallhotel.co.uk**

Hotels & restaurants

Weetwood Hall

Set within nine acres of parkland estate and built around a 17th century manor house, Weetwood Hall offers extensive 4-star hotel services and facilities, along with a conference centre. We offer three dining options: the contemporary styled Brasserie, Woodlands Restaurant, and the 'award winning' Stables Pub, serving traditional pub food."

Details

Jonathan Coxon
0113 2306000
Otley Road
Leeds
LS16 5PS
West Yorkshire
F: **0113 2306095**
E: **sales@weetwood.co.uk**
W: **www.weetwood.co.uk**

Hotels & restaurants

Wentbridge House Hotel

Wentbridge House is a beautiful four-star country house hotel, two rosette restaurant and brasserie close to the cities of Wakefield, Doncaster, Leeds and York. Set in 20 acres of gardens and grounds, Wentbridge House has 41 individually designed and decorated bedrooms as well as facilities for meetings, events and wedding receptions.

Details

James Page
01977 620444
The Great North Road
Wentbridge
Pontefract WF8 3JJ
West Yorkshire
F: **01977 620148**
E: **info@wentbridgehouse.co.uk**
W: **www.wentbridgehouse.co.uk**

Hotels & restaurants

Woodlands Hotel (Tomahawk Group)

A luxury 23 bedroom hotel set in landscaped gardens on the outskirts of Leeds. The stylish restaurant serves fresh locally sourced produce. A la carte dinner, afternoon teas and alfresco dining on the terrace is popular in the summer.

Details

Craig Squelch
0113 2381488
Gelderd Road
Gildersome, Leeds LS27 7LY
West Yorkshire
F: **0113 2536773**
E: **enquiries@woodlandsleeds.co.uk**
W: **www.woodlandsleeds.co.uk**

Did you know?

488,000

There are 488,000 pigs in the county – nearly two thirds of the English total.

els & restaurants

orkshire culpture Park

orkshire Sculpture Park's ontemporary, family friendly estaurant has panoramic views f the historic landscape and lenry Moore's monumental culptures. Using only the nest local produce, including rize winning Yorkshire lighlander beef, Whitby crab, nd Wakefield rhubarb, the estaurant serves delicious akes, chef's specials and light unches every day from 10-5pm.

etails
oe Penney
1924 832503
S.P. Trading Ltd
retton Hall, West Bretton
Vakefield
VF4 4LG
Vest Yorkshire
: **info@ysp.co.uk**
: **www.ysp.co.uk**

Conferences & events

Leeds United Football Club

Sourcing goods locally is an important part of our food policy. All fresh produce, meats, poultry, seafood are sourced locally and ethically wherever possible.

Details
Norbert Pichler
0113 3676026
Elland Road
Leeds LS11 OES
West Yorkshire
E: **conferenceandevents@leedsunited.com**
W: **www.leedsunited.com**

Outside caterers

Boutique Catering

Boutique Catering provides bespoke catering experiences for any event or occasion. We specialise in event catering, private dining, parties, product launches, barbecues, boardroom lunches and venue sourcing.

Details
Greg Lewis
0113 2637915
Carlton Mills
Pickering Street, Armley
Leeds LS12 2QG
West Yorkshire

Outside caterers

CGC Events

CGC Events (formerly Craven Gilpin) are the North's premier event caterer. We are passionate, prestigious and professional and deliver consistent high quality no matter where or no matter what. We guarantee our food and service will be to the highest standard using the freshest quality ingredients, many of which are sourced locally.

Details
Fiona Mitchell
or Julie Bray
0113 2876387
Supreme House
Lotherton Way
Garforth
Leeds LS25 2JY
E: **julie.bray@cgcevents.co.uk**
E: **fiona.mitchell@cgcevents.co.uk**
W: **www.cgcevents.co.uk**

Deli & independent grocers

Deli Central

A family run business where we make our own cakes, quiches, soups and salads daily, and our hams, beef and salmon are cooked on site. Our homemade scones, served with Rosebud Midsummer jam, and a pot of Taylor's Earl Grey loose leaf tea, are renowned locally.

Details

Tony Sykes
01924 385935
20 Northgate
Wakefield
WF1 1PQ
West Yorkshire
F: **01924 369201**
E: **info@deli-central.co.uk**
W: **www.deli-central.co.uk**

Deli & independent grocers

Doorstep Deli

An at-home sales service offering speciality foods, ingredients, treats and a party service, combining the best aspects of shopping online and in speciality delis.

Details

Becky Schofield
07765 442820
68 The Drive
Kippax, Leeds LS25 7NA
West Yorkshire
E: **beckyschofield@doorstep-deli.co.uk**
W: **www.doorstep-deli.co.uk**

Geo Middlemiss & Son

Traditional, award-winning butchers shop established in 1881, located in the heart of the thriving market town of Otley. Selling locally sourced beef, lamb and pork.

Details

Tony, Peter & Martin Middlemiss
01943 462611
3 Market Street
Otley LS21 3AF
West Yorkshire
E: **a.middlemiss@btinternet.com**
W: **www.dalesnet.co.uk**

Deli & independent grocers

Haley & Clifford Delicatessen

Our comprehensive range of Yorkshire produce includes local cheeses, local artisan baked bread, condiments and oils, delicious local cakes and chocolates and award winning fish and meats smoked in Yorkshire. We make fresh soups and salads in our kitchen daily as well as handmade sandwiches and meals to takeaway.

Details

Val Berry
0113 2370334
43 Street Lane
Roundhay
Leeds
LS8 1AP
West Yorkshire
F: **0113 2370425**
E: **val@haleyandclifford.co.uk**
W: **www.haleyandclifford.co.uk**

i & independent grocers

Harvey Nichols The Fourth Floor Cafe Bar & Foodmarket

Harvey Nichols Leeds Fourth Floor hosts the Foodmarket, Wine shop, Yo Sushi! and all day dining in the café and bar. Restaurant Tues-Sat evenings. Light treats available in the Espresso Bar.

Details

Richard Walton Allen
0113 2048000
107-11 Briggate
Leeds
LS1 6AZ
West Yorkshire
F: **0113 2048080**
W: **www.harveynichols.com**

Shaws Petroleum

Convenience stores selling good local produce. Stores in Huddersfield and Barnsley.

Details

Paul Sykes
01484 667744
Farnley House, Manor Road
Farnley Tyas
Huddersfield HD4 6UL
West Yorkshire
F: **01484 662244**
E: **paulsykes@shawspetroleum.co.uk**

Farm shops

Blacker Hall Farm Shop

At Blacker Hall Farm Shop over 90% of the food we sell is produced or prepared on the premises. The butchery, bakery and delicatessen offer a wide range of award winning local produce, with all meat coming from our own farm and other neighbouring farms. Best Farm Shop In England (Meat Trades Journal).

Details

Edward Garthwaite
01924 267202
Branch Road
Calder Grove
Wakefield
WF4 3DN
West Yorkshire
F: **01924 263849**
E: **info@blackerhall.com**
W: **www.blackerhall.com**

Farm shops

Keelham Hall Farm Shop

At Keelham Hall Farm Shop all products are sold at prices that represent true value for money right across the board – often cheaper than the supermarkets. There is something for everyone from the award winning butchery department, fresh fruit and veg selection, wines and beers, deli, chef's larder and garden centre.

Details

Victoria Robertshaw
01274 833472
Brighouse & Denholme Road
Thornton, Bradford
BD13 3SS
West Yorkshire
F: **01274 833535**
E: **enquiries@thefarmshop.net**
W: **www.keelhamhallfarmshop.co.uk**

Cleethorpes

North/ North East Lincs

There's a taste of everything for visitors who venture to North/North East Lincolnshire. Whether it's the stunning coastline, its towns or the magnificent Wolds, the region has plenty to offer, not least top notch food including award-winning Lincolnshire sausages and pies made from fresh free range pork and luxury hand-made crisps made from locally-grown potatoes.

Take a trip to Grimsby where you'll find one of the most important fish markets in Europe renowned for the quality and diversity of its fish. Then travel on south to Cleethorpes – a family fun-packed place with its popular beach and seaside facilities. Back inland, you'll find Scunthorpe and its bustling market and The Foundry shopping centre. For something a little less hectic, learn about the area's early and later history at the North Lincolnshire Museum, or take a stroll round the established evergreen and deciduous trees of Twigmoor and Broughton Woods.

And don't leave the area without exploring the Wolds – an area of outstanding natural beauty which offers an extensive range of walks taking in nature reserves, medieval villages and canals.

www.visitlincolnshire.com

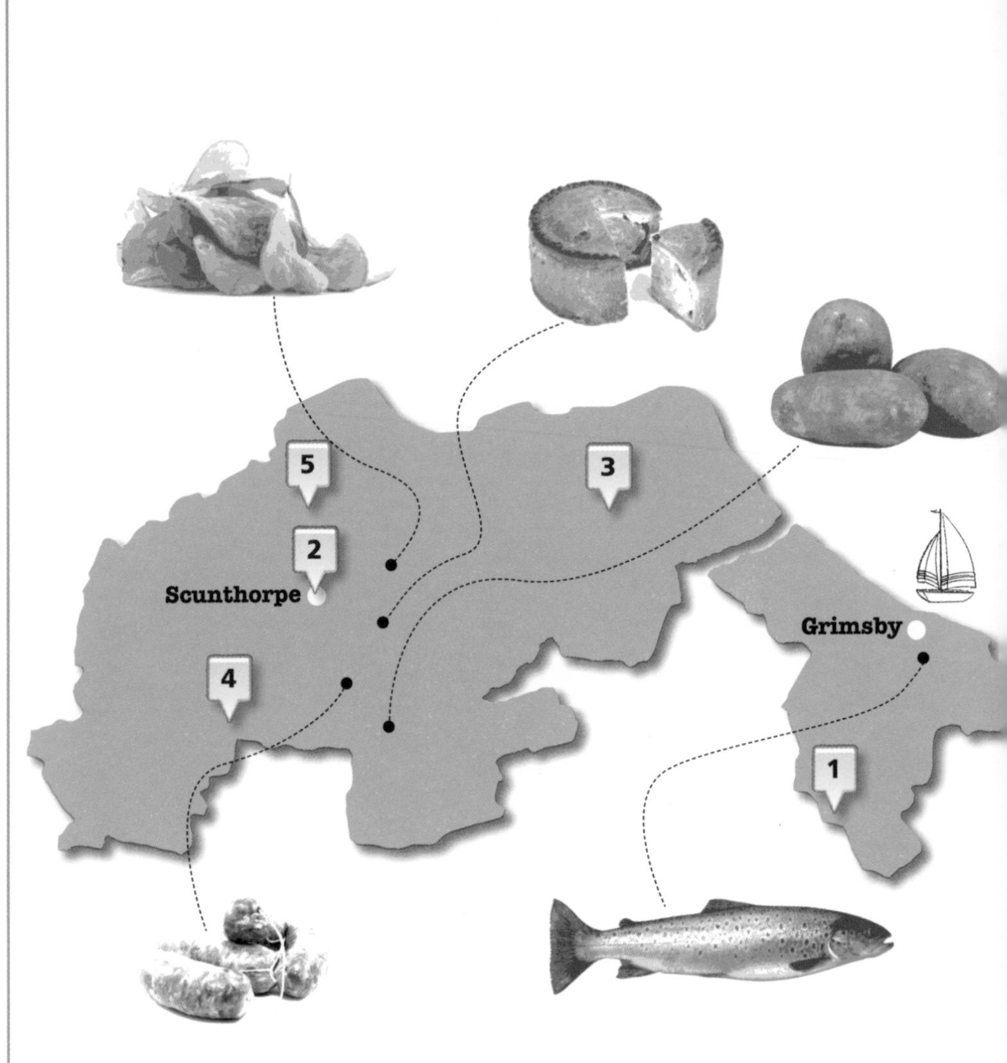
5
3
2
Scunthorpe
Grimsby
4
1

Food Highlights

1. Ideal Lincs *(see entry on page 199)*
2. Mr Huda's Surma Secret Spices *(see entry on page 198)*
3. Pipers Crisps *(see entry on page 198)*
4. Redhill Farm Free Range Pork *(see entry on page 198)*
5. Tribe *(see entry on page 199)*

Meat, poultry & game (fresh & smoked)

Pipers Crisps

We are proud to use locally grown potatoes and natural flavours, sourced from our friends who are passionate about quality; salt from Halen Mon on Anglesey, John Alvis's cheddar, cider vinegar from Julian Temperley and sweet chilli from the Genovese family in Bedfordshire.

Details
Alex Albone
01652 686960
Wellington House, Wellington Way, Elsham Wood Industrial Estate, Brigg, DN20 0SP North Lincolnshire
F: **01652 686960**
W: **www.piperscrisps.com**

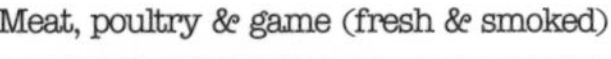

Meat, poultry & game (fresh & smoked)

Redhill Farm Free Range Pork

Redhill Farm are the real thing! Real farmers who produce everything by hand on their farm. Once tasted, customers are converted – our pork is slowly reared, succulent and full of flavour. We are popularly known at Farmers Markets as the stall with a queue! See website for nearest farmers market.

Details
Jane Tomlinson
01427 628270
Redhill Farm, Blyton Carr Gainsborough, DN21 3DT North Lincolnshire
F: **01427 628270**
W: **www.redhillfarm.com**

Preserves, honey, condiments & spic

Mr Huda's Surma Secret Spices Ltd

A range of products for both consumers and trade, bringing the authentic taste of India to your kitchen. For 2009 the range has been extended to allow businesses to take advantage of Surma Secrets with the introduction of caterin sized tubs.

Details
Mafazul Huda
01724 335492
161 Frodingham Road, Scunthorpe, North Lincs ,DN15 7NH North Lincolnshire
F: **01724 335492**
E: **info@mrhudas.co.uk**
W: **www.mrhudas.co.uk**

pared food

ribe

ribe produces South African neat products. Biltong, oerewors, Sosaties and narinated chicken are our peciality. We blend our own uring spices and marinades to nsure traditional flavours. Jo artificial flavours or reservatives are used. Our ttention to detail is reflected n the quality of our products.

Details
ichard Van Wyk
1724 734977
7886 353782
1 Earlsgate Gardens
Vinterton
cunthorpe
N15 9TN
incolnshire
: **info@biltongtribe.com**
: **www.biltongtribe.com**

Prepared food

Ideal Lincs Ltd

Specialist wholesaler and distributor of the finest fresh, frozen and ambient produce from the East Riding of Yorkshire and Humber and Lincolnshire. Supplying into multiple retailers by operating a regional food hub for Asda and the Lincolnshire Co-Operative, specialising in value added produce.

Details
Paul Davey
01507 313855
Grange Offices, Girsby Lane,
Burgh on Bain
Market Rasen
LN8 6LA
Lincolnshire
F: **0870 383 5280**
E: **paul@ideal-lincs.co.uk**
W: **www.ideal-lincs.co.uk**

Did you know?

488,000

There are 488,000 pigs in the county – nearly two thirds of the English total

Food and drink businesses in Yorkshire and Humber make producing fantastic food look simple, but in reality every tasty morsel tells a story of supreme team effort.

Behind each dish are companies who help ensure production facilities, processes and staff meet hygiene requirements, who remove or recycle waste, who package, market and distribute every little gem, and who ensure great ideas and products are properly protected.

They may not be the most obvious ingredient of Yorkshire food and drink, but specialist services are vital in guaranteeing every quality meal is the real deal.

Specialist services

This scandal will haunt the British people

a really cool company

a really cool company specialises in the bespoke delivery of temperature controlled food and pharmaceutical samples throughout the UK and Europe. Occasional deliveries and distribution, but London weekly!

Details

David Copley
0113 2886502
39 Harewood Mews
Harewood
Leeds LS17 9LY
West Yorkshire
W: **www.areallycoolcompany.co.uk**

Abacus 155 Ltd

I provide all my clients with a cost efficient, quality accountancy service, that suits their needs, which together with my experience in the food industry, means I am totally confident I can help you drive your business forward.

Details

Stuart Baldwin
08700 502212
4 Spring Bank Meadow
Ripon HG4 1HQ
North Yorkshire
E: **stuart.baldwin@abacusnetwork.co.uk**
W: **www.155.abacusnetwork.co.uk**

anniestirk

SPECIALIST FOOD PR & MARKETING

Absolutely Food PR & Marketing

Let us tell the world about your wonderful food business. As experienced food media specialists, we can offer creative but cost effective PR solutions.

- Consultancy
- PR day with a difference
- Event management
- Mystery shopper service
- Awards submissions
- Food styling & photography
- Recipe development

Details

Annie Stirk
01347 810531
07771 655756
Close House
Main Street
Stillington
York
YO61 1JU
North Yorkshire
E: **admin@absolutelyfood.co.uk**
W: **www.absolutelyfood.co.uk**

Andrew Jackson Solicitors

Business Lawyers. For your every need in forming, running, maintaining and protecting your business and personal interests. Small business or large – we can help.

Details

Hugh Smith
01482 325242
Essex House
Manor Street
Hull, HU1 1XH
East Yorkshire
F: **01482 212974**
E: **hugh.smith@andrewjackson.co.uk**
W: **www.andrewjackson.co.uk**

Bartlett Group Ltd

Bartlett is an independent, specialist insurance broker with a long and successful history of delivering insurance solutions to the UK food and drink market.

Details

Lynda Michel
0113 2585711
Broadway Hall, Horsforth
Leeds LS18 4RS
West Yorkshire
F: **0113 2585081**
E: **consumerfoodanddrink@bartlettgroup.com**
E: **tradefoodanddrink@bartlettgroup.com**
W: **www.bartlettgroup.com**

Carrot Juice

ood and drink brand packaging esign consultants – helping rands to get listed and icrease sales. We employ a nix of consumer behavioural sychology, brand strategy and esign to achieve this. We won't ore you with jargon, just inspire.

Details
Nick Lock
01943 468553
egholme, Wharfebank
usiness Centre
tley, Leeds LS21 3JP
West Yorkshire
E: **nick.lock@carrotjuicecreative.com**
W: **www.carrotjuicecreative.com**

Croner

mployment law, health & afety advice and consultancy. rom online or print information o software solutions, we an help you comply with the egal requirements relevant to our organisation.

Details
Diane Crabtree
01422 377392
Ellistones Place
Greetland
Halifax HX4 8LD
West Yorkshire
E:**diane.crabtree@**
ronerconsulting.co.uk

Crayke Kitchen

Gilli Cliff has worked with food, and as a restaurateur, broadcaster and food writer for over 20 years. She develops recipes, demonstrates to small and large crowds and inspects eateries. Her writing skills have allowed her to produce 10 cookery books.

Details
Gilli Cliff
01347 822386
Mosswood Cottage
Crayke
YO61 4TQ
North Yorkshire
E: **gilli@countrycook.co.uk**
W: **www.gillicliff.co.uk**

Design Futures

designfutures
product and packaging innovation

A team of award-winning designers offering packaging design, company branding and pack sourcing to suit budgets of all sizes. Our team have developed packaging and branding for many Yorkshire food and drink companies, including Yalp Drinks, Andrew Jones Pies, Just Puds and Glenroyd Organics.

Details
John Kirkby
0114 2256750
Sheffield Hallam University
Furnival Building
153 Arundel Street
Sheffield
S1 2NU
South Yorkshire
F: **0114 225 2718**
E: **j.kirkby@shu.ac.uk**
W: **www.dfgroup.co.uk**

Gilholm Harrison Limited

Gilholm Harrison was primarily set up to protect the Intellectual Property of individuals or small businesses – particularly new start ups. Initial consultation is free. Call 07803 986715.

Details
Tony Hanson
01904 795869
Marlborough House
Westminster Place
York Business Park
Nether Poppleton, York
YO26 6RW North Yorkshire
F: **01904 795382**
E: **tonyhanson106@tiscali.co.uk**
W: **www.gilholmharrison.com**

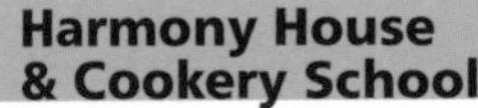

Harmony House & Cookery School

Day and residential cookery courses at Harmony House for adults and children of all abilities. Offering cookery demonstrations, home tuition, culinary team building, food hygiene training and food solutions for easy home entertaining.

Details
Hilary Finney
01904 720933
The Green, Stillingfleet
York YO19 6SH North Yorkshire
E: **hilary@harmonyhousecookeryschool.co.uk**
W: **www.harmonyhousecookeryschool.co.uk**

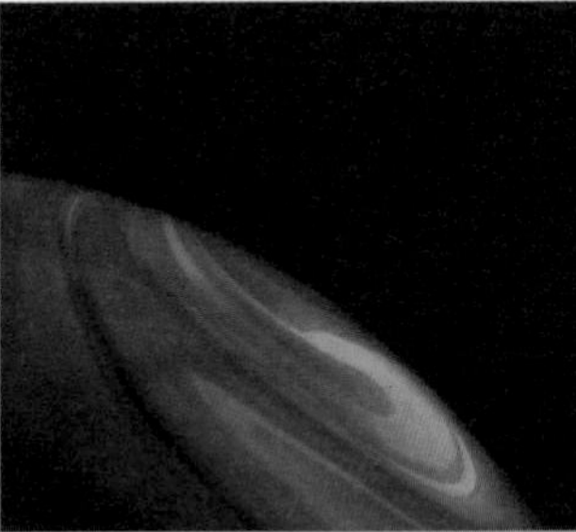

Harrison Goddard Foote

HGF is one of the UK's leading firms of Patent and Trade Mark Attorneys with offices throughout the UK. We can help shape your IP strategy and assist in identifying how the IP affairs of your business are prioritised. We can also deal with the creation, identification and protection of IP, and enhance its value to the business by appropriate management, exploitation and enforcement. For further information, or for an initial consultation, please contact Richard Wylie on 01132 330 100 or email rwylie@hgf.com

Details
Steve Gilholm
0113 233 0100
Belgrave Hall
Belgrave Street
Leeds
LS2 8DD
West Yorkshire
F: **0113 233 0101**
E: **crgraver@hgf.com**
W: **www.dfgroup.co.uk**

Huddersfield Town Centre Partnership Ltd (HTCPL)

Huddersfield Food and Drink Festival at St George's Square: 13th-16th Aug 2009, FREE. West Yorkshire's biggest food and drink festival with over 45 local and regional stallholders.

Details
Cathy Burger
01484 487933
Unit 51, The Media Centre
Northumberland Street
Huddersfield HD1 1RL
West Yorkshire
F: **01484 487935**
E: **htcpl@kirklees.gov.uk**
W: **www.foodanddrinkfestival.co.uk**

Did you know?

The world-famous Harry Ramsden fish and chip story started from a hut in Guiseley in 1928. The Ritz-style restaurant celebrated its 21st birthday by serving fish and chips to a record 10,000 people

Irene Myers & Associates

PR & Marketing
irene
myers
& associates

We make it happen… with years of experience, and an understanding and creative approach to food PR and marketing, for your business – and your budget! We combine our expertise and know-how into making you stand out from the crowd – it's about making a good business into a great business. We're only a phone call away!

Details

Irene Myers
01642 312226
Village Farm
Newby
Middlesbrough
TS8 0AD
North Yorkshire
E: **irene@irenemyerspr.co.uk**
W: **www.irenemyerspr.co.uk**

Imagen Photography Ltd

Imagen are commercial photographers specialising in food for packaging, advertising, editorial, cookery books and PR. Our studios are both equipped with a full working kitchen, client lounge,

Details

Pete Guttridge
01430 871971
5 Becklands Park
York Road
Market Weighton
YO43 3GA
East Yorkshire

Malmo Food Innovation & Technology Park

Malmo Food Park offers fledging or established food producers a professional environment for business. Our purpose built facility provides food grade units on very competitive terms, supported by an on-site manager.

Details

Rachel Field
01482 331 533

Malmo Road
Sutton Fields Industrial Estate
Hull HU7 0YN
East Yorkshire
W: **www.malmopark.co.uk**

MK (Public Relations)

MK houses a broad combination of expertise and capability within the field of PR. Our services include media relations; online communications; stakeholder engagement and advising on corporate responsibility. MK works with a large number of food and drink companies within the region, ranging from independent producers to hospitality clients with a national remit.

Details

Caroline Woffenden
0114 2756784
3A Brooklyn Works
Green Lane, Kelham Island
Sheffield
S3 8SH
South Yorkshire
F: **0114 2753019**
E: **help@mkthingshappen.co.uk**
W: **www.mkthingshappen.co.uk**

OPM Group

Multi-award winning printers of high quality self-adhesive labels, laminates, sachets, flow wrap and flexible packaging. Accredited by the British Standards Institution (BSI) and by the British Retail Consortium / Institute of Packaging (BRC / IOP) for their technical standard in supplying food packaging materials for retailer branded products (Category B).

Details

Simon Mashiter
01535 642528
Speedprint House
Halifax Road
Cross Roads, Keighley
BD22 9DH
West Yorkshire
F: **01535 643958**
E: **sales@opmlabels.com**
W: **www.opmlabels.com**

PKF UK LLP

PKF is one of the UK's leading firms of accountants and business advisers which specialise in advising the management of larger private owned businesses and smaller listed companies.

Details

James A Turner
0113 22284118
Pannell House
6 Queen Street, Leeds LS1 2TW
West Yorkshire
F: **0113 2284242**
E: **james.turner@uk.pkf.com**

Did you know?

The Great Yorkshire Show goes back

171

years. It used to tour 30 towns before the innovative decision was made in 1950 to build a permanent showground in Harrogate.

Quantech Solutions

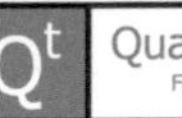

Providing local food producers and processors with route-to-market supply chain consultancy, with particular expertise in the meat sector. We can help you develop your company's strategy and marketing plan, and develop business opportunities through supply chain learning, collaboration and innovation. We have considerable experience of successfully obtaining grants for individual companies and sector organisations.

Details

Sam Hoste
01653 694490
Howe Farm
Old Malton
Malton
YO17 6RG
North Yorkshire
E: **sam.hoste@quantechsolutions.co.u**
W: **www.wholechain.co.uk**

Quantum Studio Limited

Specialists in food photography of the highest quality, whether on location or in our Leeds studio. Having a fully equipped kitchen and food stylist, we can offer new ideas to build with your product/brand. We pride ourselves on great teamwork in an easy-going environment. Thus ensuring we achieve creative images for all our clients needs.

Details

Sonia Davies
0113 2740077
Abbey Mills
Abbey Road, Kirkstall
Leeds LS5 3HP
West Yorkshire
F: **0113 2784883**
E: **info@quantumstudios.co.uk**

Red Squirrel Media

Creating unique, imaginative and highly-effective ethical branding, print and digital design – we help local retailers, producers and farmers to promote their brands and grow their business, harnessing the beauty of our region.

Details

Suzanne Hudson
0113 2461199
Blayds House
Blayds Yard, Leeds LS1 4AD
West Yorkshire
F: **01943 462075**
E: **suzanne@turnkey.eu.com**
W: **www.redsquirrelmedia.co.uk**

Stafforce Recruitment

Specialist recruitment services for the food and drink industry supplying temporary manufacturing staff, office staff and interim management staff. Working with clients such as Coke, Young's Seafood and Aunt Bessie's.

Details

Tony Boorman
01709 377177
Reginald Arthur House
Percy Street, Rotherham
S65 1ED
F: **01709 370037**
E: **tony.boorman@stafforce.co.uk**
W: **www.stafforce.co.uk**

Rollits Food Group

rollits

...more than a law firm

Rollits Food Group provide legal and commercial advice to food and drink companies, specialising in corporate, regulatory, property and employment law. Julian Wild has over 30 years experience of buying and selling food businesses, facilitating management buy-outs and financing transactions.
For more information call Julian on his mobile 07850 739 656.

Details

Julian Wild
01482 337304

Wilberforce Court
High Street
Hull
HU1 1YJ
East Yorkshire
E: **julian.wild@rollits.com**
W: **www.rollits.com**

Susan Kenyon Marketing Consultants Ltd

Ask Strategic Marketing & Research. Bespoke Market Research for food & drink and health & well-being including product tasting & benchmarking services.

Details

Susan Kenyon
01484 437424
Unit 59a, The Media Centre
7 Northumberland Street
Huddersfield HD1 1RL
West Yorkshire
F: **01484 437426**
E: **ask@susankenyon.co.uk**
W: **www.susankenyon.co.uk**

Tanfield Engineering

We offer specialist engineering services to the food, brewing and dairy industries, including the manufacture, maintenance, repair or reconditioning of all process equipment. Individual maintenance contracts available.

Details

Kari Bosworth
01677 423370
Tutin Road, Leeming Bar
Industrial Estate, Northallerton
DL7 9UJ North Yorkshire
F: **01677 423370**
E: **tanfieldengineer@aol.com**
W: **www.tanfieldenginerring.co.uk**

Thru the Line Limited

As winner of the Design Business Effectiveness Awards 2007, we believe that any of our communication has to be creative, effective and measurable. Supporting our clients every step of the way, whether your brief is to: create a new brand identity; design new packaging or sales promotional collateral and mock ups; research your market place; raise awareness of your product; increase footfall; develop meaningful relationships with buyers. 99.9% of our business is referred to us.

Details

Erika Ritchie
01943 464421
23 Pegholme Mill
Ilkley Road
Otley
LS21 3JP
West Yorkshire
W: **www.thrutheline.com**

United by Design

United by Design
A multi-disciplined graphic design agency

Providing clients with effective design and communication solutions that add value and produce return on investment. Working on creative projects that include brand identity and development, printed matter, art direction, packaging and website design. Successfully working with breweries, supermarkets, confectioners and independent producers.

Details

Owen Turner
01904 445328
First Floor Studio
11 St Pauls Terrace
York
YO24 4BL
North Yorkshire
E: **owen@ubdstudio.co.uk**
W: **www.ubdstudio.co.uk**

Yorkshire Agricultural Society

he Yorkshire Agricultural Society rganises and hosts the Great orkshire Show and Countryside ive. It also arranges a rogramme of events for choolchildren, students and eachers; and provides support o organisations connected vith agriculture.

)etails

Jigel Pulling

)1423 546201

ireat Yorkshire Showground
Iarrogate
IG2 8PW
Jorth Yorkshire
: **01423 551234**
: **heatherp@yas.co.uk**

W: **www.yas.co.uk**

Did you know?

The food and drink sector's annual contribution to the regional economy is worth £8 billion *(ONS 2008)*

deliciouslyorkshire Food Events

2009

Great Yorkshire Show	14-16 July 2009
Driffield Show	22 July 2009
Ryedale Show	28 July 2009
Bingley Show	9 August 2009
Egton Show	26 August 2009
Hull GlobalFoodFest	4-6 September 2009
Harrogate Autumn Flower Show	18-20 September 2009
Stokesley Show	19 September 2009
Countryside Live	24-25 October 2009
St Nicholas Fayre	26-29 November 2009
Knaresborough Edwardian Market	5-6 December 2009

2010

Wakefield, Food, Drink & Rhubarb Festival	February/March 2010
York Easter Market	April 2010
Harrogate Spring Flower Show	April 2010

For all the latest show information, visit

www.deliciouslyorkshire.co.uk

Farmers Markets

North

York
ork Auction Centre,
st & 3rd Saturdays
9am - 1pm

York
Parliament Street
Last Friday
9am – 4pm

Harrogate
Market Place,
2rd Thursday
9am - 4pm

Malton
The Market Place,
2nd Sunday
9am - 2pm

Northallerton
High Street,
4th Wednesday
8am - 3pm

Pateley Bridge
dderdale Showground
th Saturday/Sunday
9.30 - 2pm

Richmond
Town Square,
3rd Saturday
8am - 3pm

East

Driffield
The Showground,
1st Saturday
9am - 1pm

South Cave
2nd Saturday

Humber Bridge
Humber Bridge
viewing area
1st Sunday

South

Doncaster
Goose Hill,
1st & 3rd Wed
10am - 4pm

Sheffield
The Moor Market,
4th Sunday
10am - 4pm

Wentworth
Hague Lane,
2nd Sunday

For more farmers markets, please visit www.syfarmersmarkets.co.uk

West

Halifax
Russell Street,
3rd Saturday
8am - 4pm

Leeds
Kirkgate Market,
1st & 3rd Sunday
9am - 2pm

Otley
Market Square,
Last Sunday
9am - 1pm

Holmfirth
Holmfirth,
3rd Sunday
9am - 3pm

For more farmers markets, please visit
www.deliciouslyyorkshire.co.uk

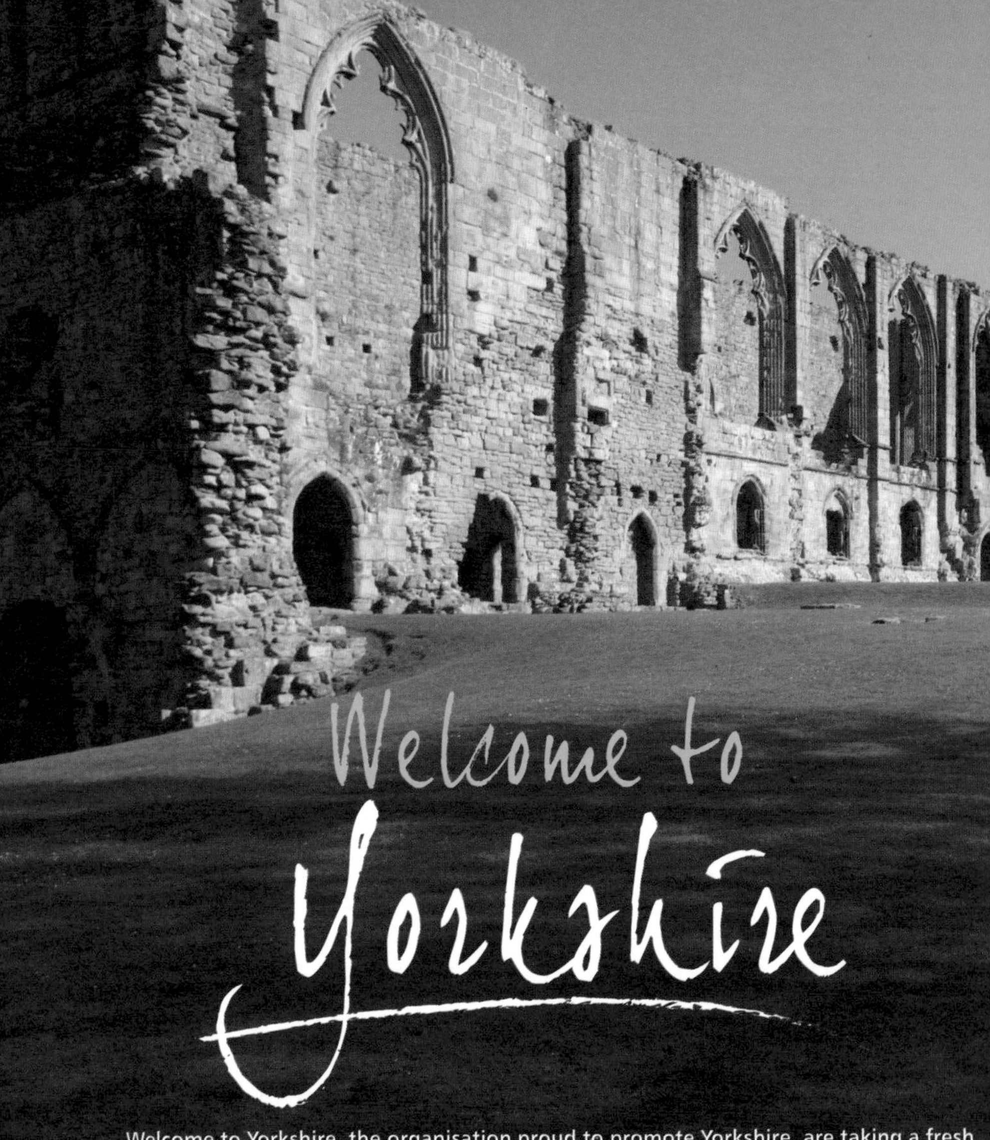
Welcome to
Yorkshire

Index

A

B

C

D

FSC
Mixed Sources
Product group from well-managed forests, controlled sources and recycled wood or fiber
Cert no. CU-COC-808383
www.fsc.org
© 1996 Forest Stewardship Council